Home Economics Basic Skills Guide Grades 7–12

Los Angeles Unified School District

Glencoe Publishing Company
Encino, California

This work was developed under a state-administered grant of federal Vocational
Education Act, Subpart 5, Section 150, Public Law 94-482, funds from the California
State Department of Education, 721 Capitol Mall, Sacramento, California 95814.
However, the content does not necessarily reflect the position or policy of that
Department or of the U.S. Department of Education; and no official endorsement
of this work should be inferred.

Publisher:

Glencoe Publishing Company
17337 Ventura Boulevard
Encino, California 91316

Printed in the United States of America

ISBN 0-02-640050-2

1 2 3 4 5 6 7 8 9   90 89 88 87 86 85

CONTENTS

PART I
HOME ECONOMICS-BASED
READING, WRITING AND MATHEMATICS SKILLS

PART II
TEACHER AND STUDENT MANAGED ACTIVITIES
IN READING, WRITING, AND MATHEMATICS

CLOTHING AND TEXTILES

PART III
STUDENT-MANAGED ACTIVITIES IN SCIENCE

PART IV
APPENDIXES

PART V
ANSWER KEY

INTRODUCTION

Home Economics Basic Skills Guide was developed and tested in the Los Angeles Unified School District over a period of six years. First published in 1979, it was revised in 1982 and in 1985. The result is the present *Guide,* which represents the work of many teachers and staff members who made suggestions, did research, field tested strategies and, finally, evaluated the results.

Home Economics Basic Skills Guide is to be used in the teaching of basic reading, writing, and computation through the vehicle of home economics. In addition, a science strand has been added at the request of many teachers who wish to broaden basic skills into that area.

This *Guide* is organized into two main sections: (1) general information on home economics-based reading, writing, and mathematics skills, and (2) specific teacher-related activities and student worksheets in reading, writing, mathematics, and science skills organized under major content areas of home economics, namely:

- Foods and Nutrition
- Parenting and Family Relationships
- Clothing and Textiles
- Consumer Education and Independent Living
- Careers

ACKNOWLEDGMENTS

Appreciation is expressed to the Basic Skills Curriculum Committee who compiled the materials for the first draft. The committee members were:

Elizabeth Adler	Fairfax High School
Suzanne Iwamura	Venice High School
Audrey Jordan	San Pedro High School
Virginia MacInnis	Pasteur Junior High School
Sylvia Reiman	Drew Junior High School
Gloria Winnick	Jefferson High School

Special appreciation is expressed to Gail Grande, Math Specialist, and Ellen Stonehill, Writing Specialist, both from Le Conte Junior High School for their contributions as professional experts to the development of this guide.

Recognition is extended to the teachers who developed, field tested and evaluated materials for this publication.

Adler, Elizabeth	Fairfax High School
Amstutz, Mary	Wilmington High School
Anderson, Marguerite	Curtiss Junior High School
Asher-Love, June	San Fernando High School
Asp, Janet	Marshall High School
Bacchetti, Noel	Garfield High School
Blythe, Relda	Olive Vista Junior High School
Bockhold, Cheryl	Westchester High School
Bradway, Nancy	Franklin High School
Brown, Mary	Venice High School
Casey, Regina	El Sereno Junior High School
Chikahisa, Evelyn	Banning High School
Credit, Josie	Huntington Park High School
Davis, Paulette	Gardena High School
Downs, Diane	Bell High School
Eifer, Elaine	Roosevelt High School
Gary, Wanda	El Sereno Junior High School
Hardrict, Verba	Washington High School
Hensley, Nancy	Franklin High School
Hill, Evagene	Garfield High School
Hilston, JoAnn	Pacoima Junior High School
Ingram, Eula	Manual Arts High School
Iwamura, Suzanne	Venice High School
James, Beth	Belvedere Junior High School
Jones, Bobbie	Drew Junior High School
Jordan, Audrey	San Pedro High School
Kontogiannis, Carole	Maclay Junior High School
Koontz, Karen	San Fernando High School
Lee, Linda	Irving Junior High School
Lindrum, George	Belmont High School
Livesay, Bette	Fairfax High School
Lonergan, Patricia	Muir Junior High School
Lynch, Joann	Wilson High School
MacInnis, Virginia	Pasteur Junior High School
McClure, Marjorie	Byrd Junior High School

Miyamoto, Kathleen	Banning High School
Mochizuki, Ellen	Palisades High School
Moreno, Mary	Eagle Rock High School
Morgan, Valerie	Carnegie Junior High School
Okui, Aki	San Fernando Junior High School
Owens, Vernida	Gage Junior High School
Ratcliff, Tommie	Olive Vista Junior High School
Reid, Janet	Sepulveda Junior High School
Ridge, Vickie	Huntington Park High School
Rivera, Noelle	Dorsey High School
Ruhr, Betty	Pacoima Junior High School
Salce, Mildred	Crenshaw High School
Smith, Marthel	San Fernando High School
Trombly, Peggy	Marina Del Rey Junior High School

Special thanks and recognition is given to Mary Snyder, Ann Hoskins and Jo-Ann Fanatino-Ruffolo, Home Economics Resource teachers, for their assistance in the development of this publication.

Particular appreciation is expressed to Kirsten Romness, Home Economics Resource Teacher, for her unflagging dedication, professional expertise, and diligent efforts in the preparation of this publication from it's inception to the final phases.

Special thanks is also extended to Beatrice Caplett, Alma Duvall and Pat Frayre, for typing and assisting with the preparation of the final draft.

Gratitude is conveyed to Donald F. Reynolds, Director, Career Education Services Unit for his cooperation in the development of this project.

MARIA REZA
Supervisor, Home Economics Education
Career Education Service Unit

JOE R. TIJERINA
Administrator
Career Education

Approved:

DR. ROBERT W. RUPERT
Assistant Superintendent
Division of Career and Continuing Education

HOW TO USE THIS GUIDE

Home Economics Basic Skills Guide has been designed to be used in any Grades 7–12 home economics-based class. The *Guide* offers a wealth of activity-based teaching suggestions (both teacher-managed and student-managed) that can be used in classes dealing with comprehensive home economics, foods and nutrition, parenting, child development, family relationships, clothing and textiles, housing and home management, consumer education, and independent living.

The *Guide* is divided into five parts.

- Part I gives an overview of the skills students need in order to read, write, and compute well.

- Part II gives specific teacher and student managed activities in the areas of reading, writing, and mathematics, as they relate to the following general categories of home economics:

  - Foods and Nutrition
  - Parenting and Family Relationships
  - Clothing and Textiles
  - Consumer Education and Independent Living
  - Careers

  Each of these categories contains many reading, writing, and mathematics activities and worksheets, arranged as follows:

  - Teacher-Managed Reading Activities
  - Teacher-Managed Writing Activities
  - Teaching Strategies for the Students Worksheets
  - Student Worksheets
    - Reading
    - Writing
    - Mathematics

- Part III contains a special section on selected science activities as they relate to various areas of home economics.

- Part IV contains fourteen appendixes that give general information on types of activities used throughout Parts I and II. These include writing filmstrips, journal writing, letter writing, and following and writing directions and lists. For convenience, there are references to this matter through Parts I and II.

- Part V contains answers for the activities in Parts II and III.

Teaching Suggestions

The *Guide* is arranged so that teachers can get to what information they need with a minimum of effort. The heart of the *Guide* is in Parts I and II.

In Part I, teachers will find information on just what reading, writing, and mathematics activities can be taught in a home economics class.

In Part II, actual teacher-managed and student-managed activities are given, the latter as worksheets. Any of these activities can be given to supplement classroom learning or as reinforcement and homework.

Strategies for present and/or teaching the activities and worksheets are built into the activities. One particular strategy that perhaps should be mentioned concerns the vocabulary lists which are included in the *Guide.* It is recommended that the vocabulary in them be learned in clusters of ten words a week, or in comparable clusters suited to your subject area and time.

PART I

HOME ECONOMICS-BASED READING SKILLS

HOME ECONOMICS-BASED WRITING SKILLS

HOME ECONOMICS-BASED MATHEMATICS SKILLS

HOME ECONOMICS-BASED READING SKILLS

The Reading Continuum is an overview of the skills students need to read well. Each reading activity objective in the *Home Economics Basic Skills Guide* is based on one or more of these skills.

The three major aspects of the Reading Continuum are *vocabulary-building, comprehension,* and *location-study skills.* After the list of skills, general information on these three major aspects is given so that the home economics teacher will be fully familiar with them.

Vocabulary-building ideas provide teachers with interesting ways to teach new words and meanings of words.

Background on *comprehension,* the most difficult aspect of reading, is included to help teachers provide activities which will increase not only subject matter knowledge but reading level as well.

Location-study skills include finding information in books and other sources, using the library effectively, and constructing outlines and bibliographies. Because there are so many situations in which these skills can be practiced in home economics classes, a detailed explanation and a list of activities related to the location of information have been included.

The teacher-managed activities and the student worksheets in this guide provide many kinds of practice for the student. Some are of the proficiency test format (display/multiple choice questions), while other provide practical, but more difficult, assignments. Students will learn home economics subject matter as they complete the reading activities found in this guide.

Reading Continuum, Grades 7-12

Readiness Skills

ENABLING SKILLS
Utilizing a variety of multimodal approaches and pictured/oral/written context, the learner:
acquires the visual acuity necessary to deal effectively with language in printed form.
visual discrimination   visual memory
acquires the auditory acuity necessary to deal effectively with the sound/symbol relationship of language as spoken/printed.
auditory discrimination   auditory memory
acquires the spoken language and semantic abilities necessary to the continued development and utilization of vocabulary and comprehension skills in all content areas.
develops perceptual and directional skills necessary for the appropriate recording and reading of printed language.

Decoding

ENABLING SKILLS
Recognizes upper/lower case alphabet letters in manuscript and cursive form.
Recognizes and uses the phonic principles of sound/symbol relationships in decoding words.
Recognizes and uses the regular and variant spelling patterns used in recording speech sounds.

Structural Analysis

ENABLING SKILLS
Recognizes and appropriately uses:
compounded and contracted words.
word additions   prefixes   suffixes   inflected forms
plural and possessive forms
abbreviated word forms

Vocabulary

ENABLING SKILLS
Utilizing vocabulary relevant to various content disciplines, the learner will recognize the categories, forms, and meaning of:
concrete and abstract words
general and specific words
prefixes un im non dis il im ir anti counter contra mis uni mono du bi tri quad quar quin multi poly semi hemi demi pre re post anti be de ex trans down sub under over super up pro co sy hyper semi anti inter intre self auto
suffixes noun er or ant ian cian ist ion ness aty ance   age ary ship ism ure
verb   ize en ate fy
adjective ess ful y er est able ible al ous ic   ant eni ate ish ive
adverb ly ward wise time side where long
root words dict graph gram port
clud clus; duc duce dict; mem; sens sent; spec; stru struct; ten tent tain tenu; vers vert
cred; fac fact fect fic fict; frag fract rupt; pen pens pend; demb simi simul; press; serve; cede ceed cess; cour cours cur curr curs; grad gred gress; ject; pel puls; trac tract
Recognizes and appropriately utilizes in various content disciplines and in real-life experiences/situations:
context clues through synonyms; antonyms; description; punctuation; signal words; comparison/contrast; example; inference
synonyms
antonyms
homonyms and homographs
analogies synonyms/antonyms; characteristics; functions, part/whole
geographical; specific/general; association; cause/effect; numerical; form class
figurative language simile; metaphor; hyperbole
onomatopoeia; alliteration
personification; euphemism
idiomatic expressions literary sources; regional sources
word origins acronyms; coining; borrowing
abbreviations common to life experiences
specific to major content disciplines

Comprehension

ENABLING SKILLS
Utilizing pictures and a variety of written materials, the student:
identifies main ideas (oral and written).
identifies details (oral and written).
recognizes capitalization/punctuation (proper nouns, sentence beginners, the word "I," period, question mark, comma, exclamation mark).
classifies information (oral and written).
arranges information in sequence (oral and written).
identifies cause and effect (oral and written).
interprets emotional reactions.
draws conclusions/predicts outcomes (oral and written).
makes inferences (oral and written).
compares/contrasts information (oral and written).
identifies reliability and validity of information.
identifies relevant/irrelevant information.
identifies literary techniques, components, types.
reacts personally to printed stimuli.
utilizes oral reading skills.

Location–Study

ENABLING SKILLS
Recognizes/uses:
parts of a book table of contents; index; glossary
library card catalogues author; title; subject; publisher; copyright date; shelving information
dictionary organization and content guide words; pronunciation key
dictionary entry word information pronunciation; word origin; part(s) of speech; definitions; illustrative sentences; derived forms; synonyms
appropriate reference materials picture files; periodicals; texts; guides to reference materials; directories; schedules
Follows written directions to complete specific tasks
Interprets and constructs pictorial representations of data tables; maps; graphs (circle, line, bar); advertisements
Develops techniques for outlining information title; major topics; major subtopics, minor entries
Recognizes and constructs bibliographies and footnotes according to generally accepted formats

BUILDING VOCABULARY

I. Types of Words

Students need to learn new *types* of words.

A. *Concrete words,* which name a thing or class of things, as opposed to abstract words. *Examples:* The word "poem" is concrete and "poetry" is abstract.

B. *Abstract words,* which express a property, quality, attribute, or relation viewed apart from the other characteristics of an object. *Examples:* Honesty; triangularity.

C. *General words,* marked by broad overall character without being limited, modified, or checked by narrow precise considerations; concerned with main elements or major matters rather than limited details; or universals rather than particulars; approximate rather than strictly accurate. *Examples:* Nutrition, budget, career.

D. *Specific words,* which fall in or constitute a category specified. *Example:* Fertilizing agents, such as nitrogen or phosphate. *Or:* Having real and fixed relationship to and usually constituting a characteristic of, that is, being peculiar to the thing or relation in questions. *Example:* The specific qualities of a drug; a specific distinction between vice and virtue; specific symptoms of a disease.

II. Parts of Words

Students need to learn the *parts* of words.

A. *Prefixes*

B. *Suffixes*

C. *Root words*

See pages 8–9 for information.

III. Word Recognition and Meaning

Students need to recognize and appropriately utilize in home economics and in real-life experiences the following:

A. *Context clues,* which are a word or group of words used to explain unfamiliar words, phrases, or sentences.

  1. *Synonyms:* Words that have the *same meaning* as other words. *Example:* big–large

  2. *Antonyms:* Words that have the *opposite meaning* of other words. *Example:* hot–cold

  3. *Description:* A statement of the properties of a thing or its relation to other things which serves to identify it. *Example:* The *crystal clear* lake was *surrounded by pine trees.*

  4. *Generalization:* A particular single item, fact, incident, or aspect that may be taken as fairly typical or representative of all of a group or type. *Example:* Children between the ages of six and eighteen are usually enrolled in school during the school year.

  5. *Definition:* A word or phrase expressing the essential nature of a person, thing, or class of persons or things. It is the answer to the question "What is X?"

Example: Panfrying is a method for cooking meat in a small amount of fat in a skillet.

6. *Inference:* The act of passing from one or more propositions, statements, or judgments considered as true to another; the truth of which is believed to follow from that of the former. *Example:* Carol was treated like Cinderella. (The inference is that she was mistreated.)

7. *Comparison/Contrast: Comparison* means that two or more things are alike, while *contrast* means that two or more things are different. *Example:* Winesap and pippin are fruit and they are apples. Oranges and apples are both fruit, but not the same type.

8. *Signal word:* A speech sound that communicates a meaning or a difference in meaning. *Examples:* the *s* of *pins;* the *hood* of *childhood.*

9. *Punctuation:* In written or printed matter, the act, practice, or system of inserting various standardized marks or signs into sentences or clauses by means of punctuation marks.

B. *Synonyms:* See above.

C. *Antonyms:* See above.

D. *Homonyms:* One or more words spelled and pronounced alike but different in meaning. *Example:* A *pool* of water; a game of *pool.*

E. *Analogy:* The inference that if two or more things agree with one another in one or more aspects, they will probably agree in yet other respects. *Example:* The classroom was like a beehive.

F. *Figurative language:* The transference in sense from the literal, or plain, to the abstract, or hypothetical, as by the expression of one thing in terms of another, with which it can be regarded as analogous.

1. *Simile:* A figure of speech comparing two essentially unlike things; often introduced by "like" or "as." *Example:* He is *as good as gold.*

2. *Metaphor:* A figure of speech in which a word or phrase denoting one kind of object or action is used in place of another to suggest a likeness or analogy between them. *Example:* The ship *plows* the seas.

3. *Hyperbole:* Extravagant exaggeration that may depict the impossible as actual. *Example:* A *mile-high* ice cream cone.

4. *Onomatopoeia:* Words which are an imitation of natural sounds; the naming of a thing or action by a more or less exact reproduction of the sound associated with it. *Examples:* Buzz, hiss, purr.

5. *Alliteration:* The repetition of a sound or consonant in two or more neighboring words or syllables. *Examples:* Wild and wooly; beautiful baby.

6. *Personification:* Giving personal qualities (personality) to a thing or abstract idea. *Example:* The flames *ate up* the house.

7. *Euphemism:* The substitution of an agreeable or inoffensive word or expression for one that is harsh, indelicate, or otherwise unpleasant or taboo; a polite or tactful way to avoid saying something that is

unpleasant, painful, or a frightening reality. *Examples:*
"Pass away" for die, "underprivileged" for poor.

G. *Idiomatic expressions* are those which have a special
meaning, and this meaning cannot be understood
completely by looking at the individual words in the
idiom. *Examples:* Died down, opened up, ran across, go
in for, kept an eye on, lost track of, play it by ear, flesh
and blood, pins and needles, big shot, white lie, eager
beaver, cut and dried, free and easy, level-headed, now
and again, by and large.

IV. Origins of Words

Students need to appreciate the where and how of the *origins
of words.* Words enter the English language in many ways,
including the following:

A. *Via acronyms:* The first letter of each word in a group of
words is used to form a new word. *Example:* NASA, for
National Aeronautics and Space Administration.

B. *Via coining:* Two words are combined into one new word,
with some of the letters from each word dropped. *Example:*
Smoke plus fog is now called smog.

C. *Via borrowing* from other languages. Borrowing is probably
the most frequent way in which words have become part of
the English language. *Example:* Part, from the Latin *Partire,*
meaning "to divide."

V. Language Changes

Students need to recognize and appreciate how language changes
because of custom or the passage of time.

A. *Sounds change. Example:* There is a current tendency to
drop the middle syllable in a word, such as the first *e* in
"omelet," or the *au* in "restaurant." *Example:* Eighty years
ago, a word like "courtesy" was pronounced *COURT*-esy,
not *CURT*-esy, as it is today.

B. *Meanings change* through:

1. *Amelioration:* The meaning has been elevated. *Example:*
A knight was once any youth, but today it is a specially
appointed person.
2. *Pejoration:* The meaning has been degraded. *Example:*
"Immaculate" once meant "pure," as in "pure of heart,"
but now it usually means "spotlessly clean," as in
"laundry."
3. *Generalization:* The meaning is no longer specific.
Example: "Shipped" once meant to send on a ship, but
now it refers to sending an item by any means of
transportation.
4. *Specialization:* The meaning is no longer a general term
which covers many categories: it means a specific
category. *Example:* "Meat" once meant any food; it
now is one food category.
5. *Euphemism:* The word is now more agreeable (pleasant,
delicate) than previously, because of general usage.
Example: "Pass away" for die.
6. *Hyperbole:* Exaggerations have become acceptable. *Example:*
Frequent use of the word "millions" or "billions," when
the real quantity may be closer to a dozen or one hundred.

VI. Abbreviations

The students need to recognize and use abbreviations.

A. Abbreviations can come from real-life experiences.

B. Abbreviations can come from various content disciplines.

VOCABULARY—EXAMPLES

Utilizing vocabulary relevant to various content disciplines, the learner will recognize the categories, forms, and meaning of prefixes, suffixes, and root words.

Prefixes

A sound or sequence of sounds, or in writing a letter or sequence of letters, occurring as a bound form attached to the beginning of a word, base, or phrase, and serving to produce a derivative word or an inflectional form.

Negative Prefixes:

*un*notched
*im*perfect, *im*potent
*non*washable
*dis*charge
*il*legal
*in*hospitable
*ir*rational
*counter*feit
*mis*carriage

Quantitative Prefixes:

*uni*form
*mono*filament
dual-duty
*bi*lateral
*tri*acetate
*quad*ruplets
*qua*rt
*quin*tuplets
*multi*filament
*poly*ester
semi-annual

Time Prefixes:

*pre*test
*re*peat
*post*partum

Directional Prefixes:

*be*tween
*de*scend
*ex*terior
*trans*action
*down*stairs
*sub*cutaneous
*under*lining
*over*lay
*super*impose
*up*surge
*pro*ceed

Conditional Prefixes:

*co*habit
*sy*nonymous
*hyper*active
semi-soft
*inter*laced
*in*trepid
self-concept
*auto*matic

Suffixes

Endings to words which make them nouns, verbs, adjectives, or adverbs.

Noun Suffixes: The name of a person, animal, plant, place, thing, substance, quality, idea, action, or state.

sell*er*	good*ness*
sen*sor*	avoid*ance*
milit*ant*	cour*age*
sectar*ian*	second*ary*
mathemati*cian*	wor*ship*
futur*ist*	botul*ism*
selec*tion*	clo*sure*

Verb Suffixes:

stabil*ize*	decor*ate*
awak*en*	satis*fy*

Adjective Suffixes: Adjectives modify a noun to qualify it.

wonder*ful*	sens*ual*
ever*y*	danger*ous*
strong*er*	terrif*ic*
fast*est*	pli*ant*
capa*ble*	desper*ate*
edi*ble*	baby*ish*
	produc*tive*

Adverb Suffixes: Adverbs modify verbs, adjectives, adverbs, prepositions, phrases, clauses, and sentences.

careful*ly*	along*side*
for*ward*	no*where*
cross*wise*	head*long*
over*time*	

Root Words

The simple element inferred as the basis from which a word is derived by phonetic change or by extension; the simple element (as Latin *sta*) inferred as common to all the words of a group in a language (as in Latin "Stamus," meaning "we stand"): *st*and, *sta*tion, *sta*tionary, *sta*tic, etc.

edict	*struct*ure	*frag*ment	*court*yard
*graph*ic	*atten*tion	*frac*ture	*cour*se
*stam*mer	pa*tent*	*rup*ture	*cur*rent
*port*ly	re*tain*	*open*	*cur*riculum
in*clude*	*tenu*re	*pen*sive	*curs*ive
*clus*ter	*vers*atile	ap*pend*age	*grad*uation
de*duc*tion	*vert*ical	*simi*lar	in*gred*ient
de*duce*	*cred*it	*simu*late	aggres*sive*
pre*dict*	*fac*ing	im*press*ion	re*ject*
*mem*ber	*fact*ual	con*serve*	re*pel*
*sens*ory	per*fect*	pre*cede*	im*pulse*
*senti*ment	*effect*	suc*ceed*	*trac*er
*spec*trum	*fic*tion	*cess*pool	re*tract*
*struc*k			

BUILDING VOCABULARY

Vocabulary can be built by utilizing a variety of teaching strategies.

1. Select about ten words per week which relate to the subject matter of the week.

   a. Print the words on a large poster, large enough so the words can be seen across a classroom. Students practice spelling the words as well as looking up their definitions.
   b. Prepare a "master" for each week, with spaces for synonyms and/or antonyms, as well as definitions.

2. Make a "Q-sort" by dividing an 8½" x 11" sheet of paper into 16 sections. Write one word per section, perhaps on one or two home economics topics. Run off and give each student a copy of the sheet to cut apart. Students then "sort" the words into various stacks, depending on the subject matter. For example, in "food," categories could be "Foods I Like," "Foods I Dislike," and "Foods I've Never Tasted." The more words, the more interesting the ensuing discussion! Have the students store each "set" in an envelope to be used later.
3. Provide students with master vocabulary lists. Have them underline all the prefixes, suffixes and root words. (See pages 8–9.)
4. After the students know and/or have written the definitions of the words on pages 8–9, they should use the words in a sentence.
5. Spelling tests should include all current words, plus a selection of words previously learned.
6. Students can use new words in stories, poems, or articles which they write. Use the subject matter of home economics to turn the students on to a love of words. The following poem is a good example.

TOMATO

The tomato is a puffy but delicate vegetable.
The seeds of the tomato are the hardest seeds
to pick up in the world.

Yes, tomatoes can be stubborn at times,
especially when you try to cut them open;
they would rather hold their breath than let
you get a word in edgewise.

But I think that we tolerate them for the
flavor, which is unsurpassable and can never
be topped with anything except salad dressing
occasionally.

DAWN ANDERSON, Grade 12

Notice the use of both *concrete* and *abstract* words ("seeds" vs. "stubborn") as well as *general* and *specific* words ("vegetable" and "tomato"). Notice the *adverbial suffix* "wise" in edgewise. The tomato *description* is clarified with "puffy but delicate." "The hardest seeds to pick up in the world" is *hyperbole,* to an extent.

Personification is found in the phrase, "they would rather hold their breath than let you get a word in edgewise." The *prefix* "un" changes the meaning of the basic word "surpassable" to a negative.

Even a poem as seemingly simple (*alliteration*) as "Tomato" has many components, all of which are part of vocabulary skill building. Correct spelling and definitions are only a small part of the wonderful world of words!

IMPROVING COMPREHENSION

Although most educators agree that comprehension is the essence of reading, there are so many levels of comprehension and such a wide range of conceptual development among students that assessing student achievement in reading is a difficult task.

Teachers can begin to deal with the problems of teaching reading by becoming aware of the activities that students should be able to perform at the different levels of reading (competency-based education).

I. Literal Comprehension

Literal comprehension involves the understanding of what the author actually said in words. When a student can perform the following competencies, he or she has reached the level of literal comprehension.

A. He or she can identify main ideas which tell what the paragraph, story, or article is about:

1. in paragraphs,
2. by selecting the best title,
3. by matching a picture with the paragraph that describes it,
4. by selecting the statement(s) that best express the main idea.

B. He or she can identify details which explain or describe something. The details often answer the questions *who, what, which, when, where, why* and *how:*

1. in a sentence,
2. in paragraphs,
3. in illustrations.

C. He or she recognizes correct capitalization and punctuation (capital letters give special attention to a letter or letters in a word; punctuation marks are used to help make the meaning clearer):

1. capitalization for proper nouns, sentence beginners, and the word "I,"
2. punctuation marks such as question marks, commas, exclamation marks, colons, and semicolons.

D. He or she can classify information, that is, arrange similar types of information into groups or categories:

1. under one heading for like or similar things, objects, or ideas,
2. under one time frame to show which events happened at the same time,
3. under one place frame to show which events happened at the same place.

E. He or she can arrange information in sequence, which is the order in which one thing follows another:

1. in chronological order, such as recipes:

   a. beginning to end,
   b. end to beginning,
   c. flashback;

2. in spatial order:

    a. maps,
    b. sketches,
    c. outlines;

3. in expository order:

    a. cause to effect,
    b. effect to cause,
    c. details to general (inductive),
    d. general to detail (deductive);

4. in alphabetical order;
5. in numerical order.

F. He or she can identify literary techniques, components, and types.

II. Inferential Comprehension

Literal comprehension involves the understanding of what the author meant. Inference is thinking beyond the facts that are written. It is determining what the reading content suggests that is not stated directly. This is one of the most important and most difficult levels of comprehension because the main ideas are not always directly stated. When a student can perform the following competencies, he or she has reached the level of inferential comprehension:

A. He or she can identify cause and effect relationships:

1. Cause is what makes something happen.
2. Effect is the result of what happens.

B. He or she can anticipate what is to follow in the written material.

C. He or she can determine the theme or main idea(s), even if not stated directly.

D. He or she can compare and contrast information:

1. Compare means to show how two or more things or ideas are alike.
2. Contrast means to show how two or more things or ideas are different.

E. He or she can determine the time, place, and mood from clues provided by the author.

F. He or she can determine the motives of characters or real people from clues provided by the author.

G. He or she responds to imagery, by "living vicariously" through the words and the ideas conveyed by the words.

H. He or she can empathize with the characters.

I. He or she can interpret his or her own emotional reactions to written material.

J. He or she reacts personally to written stimuli.

III. Applicative Comprehension

Applicative comprehension is the level at which the reader can use what the author has said. When the student can perform in the following competencies, he or she has reached the level of applicative comprehension:

A. Students can determine the most logical thing to do.

B. Students can determine the most interesting thing to do.

IV. Analytical Comprehension

Analytical comprehension involves determining the validity of what the author said. When the student can perform the following competencies, he or she has reached the level of analytical comprehension.

A. He or she can identify the reliability and validity of information; he or she can make authenticity judgments.

B. He or she can distinguish between fact and opinion.

C. He or she can identify relevant and irrelevant information:

1. Relevant information is that which is important, useful, or meaningful.
2. Irrelevant information is that which is not important, useful, or meaningful.

D. He or she can analyze propaganda for the following:

1. *Bad name;* unpleasant connotations. *Examples:* lemon, yellow, communist, un-American.
2. *Glad names* or glittering generalities; pleasant connotations. *Examples:* marvelous, all-American, pleasingly plump.
3. *Testimonial;* tribute to a person, place, or thing and recommended by a famous person. *Example:* athlete advertising Wheaties.
4. *Transfer:* pairing a highly regarded person or symbol with a product being promoted. *Examples:* research proves that nine out of ten doctors use . . .; an eagle on a dictionary cover.
5. *Plain folks:* a technique to make a person appear to be ordinary; one of the common people; an appeal to the ordinary citizen who is neither glamorous nor rich.
6. *Card stacking:* Telling only the points that are in your favor and the ones that show up the worst attributes of your opponent.
7. *Bandwagon:* To appeal to people's desire to be a part of the "in crowd."

E. He or she can analyze fallacies of reasoning:

1. In *mistaken causal relationships. Example:* A large vocabulary is equivalent to success in life. Children who know the alphabet when they enter school are likely to be better readers. Therefore, knowledge of the alphabet is equal to success in reading and the acquiring of a large vocabulary.
2. In *statistics. Example:* Graduates of Harvard University earn an average of $50,000 a year. (The questions that need to be raised are: How was this information obtained? Which type of average was used—mean, median or mode? Is income a factor of education or inheritance, etc.?)
3. In *false analogies,* wherein two things being compared are not comparable. *Example:* Is motorcycle riding dangerous? No, the death rate of motorcycle riders is slightly below that of the general public.

4. When a statement is *oversimplified,* usually the result of failure to examine all possibilities. The statement has some truth, but not enough. *Example:* Either the husband is the boss, or the wife is.

5. When a person or a group is *stereotyped,* which over-emphasizes qualities that people are said to have in common or which deemphasizes individual uniqueness.

6. When the author *ignores the question.* The author digresses into an irrelevant argument to make a point.

7. When the author *begs the question.* The author evades a question by basing arguments on faulty generalizations. *Example:* Why do you dislike philosophy? Because it is boring, and I hate boring subjects.

8. When making *hasty generalizations,* which are conclusions based on insufficient evidence. *Example:* John, Frank, and Carl received A's in class. That proves boys are smarter than girls.

LOCATION-STUDY SKILLS

When students have mastered good location-study skills, they can recognize and use appropriate sources of information to find out what they need to know. Among these sources are *people* (teachers, librarians), *places* (library, city hall), or *written materials* (textbooks, dictionaries).

A. Students can recognize and use:

1. Parts of a book:

   a. Title, author, and publisher page
   b. Library of Congress/copyright page
   c. Introductory information or preface
   d. Table of contents
   e. General organization of book
   f. Glossaries
   g. Index
   h. Appendix
   i. Other, as included

2. Library Card Catalog:

   a. Three basic classifications in card catalog:

      1. author
      2. title
      3. subject matter

   b. Read card for specific information:

      1. publisher
      2. copyright date
      3. shelving information

3. Dictionaries (including the various types of dictionaries):

   a. Organization
   b. Content:

      1. guide words
      2. pronunciation key

    c. Word entry information:

        1. pronunciation
        2. word origin
        3. parts of speech
        4. definitions
        5. illustrative sentences
        6. derived forms/synonyms, etc.

  4. Other appropriate reference materials:

    a. Picture files
    b. Periodicals
    c. Textbooks
    d. Guides to reference materials (such as the *Readers' Guide to Periodical Literature*)
    e. Directories (such as the telephone book)
    f. Schedules (such as for the bus or train)

B. Students can follow written directions to complete specific tasks. *Example:* The student can read a map and get from point A to point B. *Example:* The student can read the directions and successfully build a model plane, a piece of furniture, etc.

C. Students can interpret and construct pictorial representations. This means they can tell what a picture or illustration is about, or they can draw a correct map so that someone else can go from point A to point B:

  1. Data
  2. Tables
  3. Maps
  4. Graphs (circle, bar, line)
  5. Advertisements
  6. Signs

D. Student develops techniques for outlining information:

  1. Selects a title
  2. Determines major topics
  3. Determines major subtopics
  4. Determines minor entries
  5. Utilizes correct format for placing topics into outline

E. Students can recognize and construct bibliographies and footnotes according to generally accepted formats.

  1. Bibliographies

    a. Books
    b. Periodicals

  2. Footnotes

    a. First entries
    b. Second entries

ACTIVITIES RELATING TO LOCATION
OF INFORMATION

To help students prepare for the proficiency exams, teachers may plan exercises to give students practice in locating information in or on:

1. Yellow pages of telephone directory
2. Telephone directory index pages
3. Dictionary
4. Cookbook index pages
5. Textbook index pages
6. Appendixes in textbooks
7. Foreword in textbooks
8. Pattern guide sheets
9. Pattern envelopes
10. Recipe analysis
11. Newspaper and magazine advertisements relating to subject studies
12. Public service organization, brochures, etc.
13. Infant formula instructions
14. TV schedules
15. Highway maps
16. Freeway and street maps
17. Telephone area code map
18. Post office ZIP code book
19. Motor vehicle driver instruction publication
20. Warranties and guarantees
21. W-2 Wage and Tax Statement

HOME ECONOMICS-BASED WRITING SKILLS

The Writing Continuum, upon which the writing activities in this guide are based, is divided into three parts: *writing tasks* (the four domains of composition), *composing skills,* and *enabling language skills.*

Home economics students will benefit if they have the opportunity to write in each of the four domains. In addition, nearly all the composing skills and the enabling language skills can be practiced in home economics writing assignments. The more opportunity students have to practice these tasks and skills, the better they will be able to write.

Tasks which are particularly suited to home economics activities have been summarized. Consumer complaint letters, for example, are part of the continuum and thus have validity both from the consumer point of view and as a writing assignment.

The section, Helpful Hints on Teaching Writing to Home Economics Students, provides practical techniques for teaching writing to secondary students.

The teacher-managed activities and the student worksheets in this guide provide many kinds of practice for the student. The Appendix contains strategies for teaching writing that are common to all areas of home economics. In the Appendix you will also find additional student worksheets. These worksheets should be distributed when you give assignments having to do with filmstrips, business letters, and maps.

Writing Continuum, Grades 7-12

Writing Tasks
(The Four Domains of Composition)

IN THE SENSORY/DESCRIPTIVE DOMAIN, THE STUDENT WRITES:

Observation notes on the physical scene.

Paragraphs of observation on a physical scene.

Simple forms of unrhymed poetry.

Simple rhymed poetry.

Journal entries.

Interpretations of pictures and objects.

Advertising copy, using sensory words.

Observations on a physical scene, using two senses.

Journal entries which include both observation and personal interpretation.

Character sketches.

Paragraphs of description, using more than two senses.

Paragraphs that employ metaphor and other figures of speech.

Descriptions of personal feelings and moods, using sensory words.

Poetry of observation.

Paragraphs that use examples to illustrate senses and feelings.

Paragraphs that extend metaphor to clarify experience.

Essays of personal response to complex stimuli (music, modern art).

Description of a setting that reflects a mood.

Paragraphs of observation focused on a single impression (poverty, greed, arrogance).

Comparisons/contrasts of two persons, settings, objects, or other subjects.

IN THE IMAGINATIVE/NARRATIVE DOMAIN, THE STUDENT WRITES:

Anecdotes of personal experiences.

Folktales, myths, fables.

Dialogues, utilizing two voices.

Captions to pictures or cartoons.

Short summaries of acts or events.

Objective accounts of an experience.

Short autobiographical sketches.

Imaginative diary entries of fictional characters.

Short narratives and short short stories.

Dialogues to develop a conflict.

Capsule stories (reconstructions of a story implied in a picture or a cartoon).

Dramatic monologues.

Poetic narratives (ballads, etc.).

Narratives retelling a humorous incident.

Narratives relating the significance of one's own personal experience.

Interpretations of experiences of another person.

Short narratives, incorporating dialogue.

Narratives inventing humorous incidents.

Personal essays (literary).

Vignettes that emphasize mood or symbol.

Biographical or autobiographical narratives to persuade or convince.

Short short stories with emphasis on character.

Interior monologues.

Narratives employing irony, satire.

Narratives employing illustrations or allusions to make a point.

Memoirs.

IN THE PRACTICAL/INFORMATIVE DOMAIN, THE STUDENT WRITES:

Friendly letters (invitations, acceptances of invitations, acknowledgments of gifts, "bread-and-butter" notes).

Brief instructions for making or doing something.

Directions to a place.

Consumer complaint letters of simple nature.

Summaries of short written reports.

Simple business and school forms.

Brief statements of personal qualifications (for class or school office).

Notes from a class textbook.

News reports.

Simple business letters of inquiry, explanation, request.

Evaluations of self after completion of a unit of work.

Directions with use of a map.

Notes on class discussion.

Paragraphs describing personal qualifications for a job or office.

Completion of standard business forms for adults.

Letters seeking recommendations for job or college application forms.

Summaries/minutes of class or committee discussions.

Essay responses for tests.

Notes on formal lectures.

Reports of an interview.

Explanations of a basic process.

Letters of application for job or college.

Autobiographical sketches for college applications.

Job-related reports (sales reports, police reports, etc.).

Compilation of job résumé.

Precis and abstracts.

IN THE ANALYTICAL/EXPOSITORY DOMAIN, THE STUDENT WRITES:

Paragraphs of simple exposition.

Short paragraphs of personal opinion.

Paragraphs of persuasion.

Editorials for the school paper.

Short reviews (movies, television shows, books).

Paragraphs of persuasion through use of reasons.

Editorials for a community paper.

Paragraphs developing opinions or values supported by specific facts.

Paragraphs of observation/interpretation based on concrete stimuli (picture, political cartoon, object).

Short narratives that draw a conclusion.

Three-paragraph expositions (little theme).

Editorials for a wider audience.

Brief literary analyses.

Short papers, using a library source.

Paragraphs of several types leading to a conclusion (descriptive, narrative).

Essays revealing cause and effect.

Essays defining/illustrating abstract values.

Essays defending one's own values.

Analyses of character based on concrete details.

Arguments on a complex topic.

Literary analyses.

Short library papers based on two or three sources.

Editorials for national audiences.

Critical analyses of quotations, values, opinions.

Analyses of a problem leading to a conclusion.

Explanations of a complex process (e.g., historical development, economic or political effects).

Essays of extended definition.

Logical persuasions/arguments (literary, political, social).

Personal essays (in literary style).

Essays of classification.
Short library papers based on several different sources.

Composing Skills

Lists examples/details that relate to a topic.
Groups examples/details that relate to each other.
Lists reasons for an opinion.
Recognizes and employs figurative language.
Employs vocabulary appropriate to a specific audience.
Arranges narratives in chronological order.
Composes strong beginning and ending sentences.
Employs words dealing with the five senses.
Composes appropriate titles.
Lists and uses words that rhyme.
Employs accepted forms of the friendly letter.
Employs accepted forms of the business letter.
Completes simple business and school forms.
Differentiates between connotations and denotations.
Composes topic sentences using key words.
Composes effective clinching sentences.
Limits topics for paragraphs.
Develops topics by stating reasons for opinions.
Selects details relevant to a topic sentence.
Uses simple transitional devices within a paragraph.
Assumes a voice not necessarily one's own.
Limits thesis for a two- or three-paragraph essay.
Writes a thesis statement.
Writes topic sentences related to a thesis.
Employs relevant details in paragraphs.
Develops paragraphs by means of examples.
Develops paragraphs by means of chronology.
Understands difference between fact and opinion.
Bases judgments on concrete evidence.
Practices completing business forms for adults.
Varies kinds of supporting details (facts, reasons, illustrations, observations).
Develops paragraphs by different methods (examples, definitions, spatial, logical, relative importance).
Uses effective transitions in a series of paragraphs.
Maintains point of view (role, stance, tone).
Chooses vocabulary appropriate for a mode/audience.
Develops introductory and concluding paragraphs.
Maintains consistency throughout essay (purpose, audience, tone, subject).
Uses concrete terms to define abstract ideas.

Compiles short bibliographies.
Uses figurative language appropriate to the subject.
Employs comparisons/contrasts to support a thesis.
Uses analogy, induction, deduction to develop a thesis.
Qualifies conclusions of others or one's own.
Assembles data from several different sources for a short library paper.
Selects, quotes, and acknowledges appropriately from outside sources.

Enabling Language Skills

Composes complete sentences.
Uses a variety of basic sentence patterns.
Expands simple sentences by compounding various elements.
Understands, constructs, and punctuates basic compound sentences (and, or, but).
Uses simple modifiers in sentences.
Composes sentences in which subjects and verbs agree.
Employs standard pronoun forms (cases).
Uses pronouns that agree with their antecedents.
Uses common idioms acceptably.
Generalizes basic spelling rules.
Punctuates correctly items in a series, dates, and addresses.
Capitalizes appropriately in sentences, quotations, and other common contexts.
Employs appropriate terminal punctuation marks.
Varies sentence patterns, using compound sentences.
Understands construction of and employs prepositional phrases appropriately.
Distinguishes clause/phrase from the sentence.
Subordinates ideas by employing adverb clauses.
Uses adverb clauses in various places for clarity and emphasis.
Distinguishes complex sentences from simple and compound sentences.
Uses active verbs appropriately.
Maintains consistency in verb tenses.
Varies sentence patterns for clarity and emphasis (simple, compound, complex).
Employs verbal phrases for economy and maturity.
Subordinates ideas by employing adjective clauses.
Punctuates complex sentences.
Employs punctuation in transcribing conversation.
Uses the compound-complex sentence for economy or variety.
Constructs compound sentences, employing semicolon and conjunctive adverb.
Employs appositives.
Uses the passive voice.

Uses commas with appositives and other parenthetical expressions.
Uses punctuation marks for quoting sources.
Employs parallel structure in coordinate elements of a sentence.
Understands structure of and employs complex noun formations (noun clauses, infinitives).

SUMMARY OF WRITING TASKS

Herewith is a summary of the writing activities, in the four domains of composition, that can be taught through home economics content.

Sensory/Descriptive Domain

1. *Observations* on the physical scene:
   - sentences and paragraphs
   - use of one or more senses
2. *Poetry:* simple unrhymed and rhymed
3. *Journal entries*
4. *Interpretations* of pictures and objects
5. *Advertising copy,* using sensory words
6. *Descriptions* of personal feelings and moods, using sensory words in sentences and paragraphs
7. Paragraphs of *observation* focused on a single impression (e.g., poverty, greed, arrogance)
8. *Comparisons/contrasts* of two persons, settings, objects, etc.

Imaginative/Narrative Domain

1. *Anecdotes* of personal experiences
2. *Captions* to pictures or cartoons
3. Short *summaries* of acts or events
4. Objective *accounts* of an experience
5. Short *autobiographical* sketches
6. *Narratives* relating the significance of one's own personal experience
7. *Memoirs*

Practical/Informative Domain

1. *Letters:*

   - Friendly
   - Consumer complaint
   - Business: inquiry, explanation, request, etc.
   - Seeking recommendations: job or college
   - Applications: job or college

2. *Instructions* for making or doing something
3. *Directions* to a place, without and with a map
4. *Summaries/minutes*

   - short written reports
   - class or committee discussions

5. *Forms,* student and adult types for business and/or school
6. *Statements* of personal qualifications for class or school in sentences and paragraphs

7. *Notes*

   - from a class textbook
   - on class discussion
   - on formal lectures

8. News *reports*
9. Self-*evaluation* after completion of a unit of work
10. *Essay test* responses
11. *Reports* of an interview
12. *Explanation* of a basic process
13. *Autobiographical* sketches for college applications
14. Job-related *reports,* e.g., sales
15. Compilation of *job résumé*

Analytical/Expository Domain

1. *Paragraphs* of

   - simple exposition
   - personal opinion
   - persuasion
   - developing opinions or values supported by single facts
   - observation/interpretation based on concrete stimulus (picture, etc.)

2. *Editorials* in

   - school paper
   - community paper

3. *Reviews* of movies, television shows, books, etc.
4. Short *papers* using one or more library resources
5. *Essays* revealing cause and effect

   - defending one's own values

6. *Analysis* of problem leading to conclusion

HELPFUL HINTS ON TEACHING WRITING

Steps in the Writing Process

Step A.

Always begin with prewriting experiences. Students must know what they are writing about and must feel sure that they have something to say *before* they write. Thus, a simple reading assignment, a class discussion, a small group discussion, a teacher or student demonstration, or a journal entry may suffice. In addition, listed below are two of many other possible prewriting techniques.

Magic Circle

The teacher and students form a circle. The teacher structures the ensuing conversation by saying, for example, "My favorite food is spaghetti. I like it because . . . ." He or she then turns to the student on his or her right, who says, "My favorite food is . . . . I like it because . . . ." Thus it goes, around the circle. Next, the students return to their desks and write about their favorite foods.

Clustering

Clustering is a written form of brainstorming. It is less restrictive than a traditional linear outline and seems to help students get started. The student places the key word on a page and then rapidly writes words and phrases around it. Since this is timed (anywhere from 3–6 minutes), it forces students to cast off their inhibitions and break through their writing blocks.

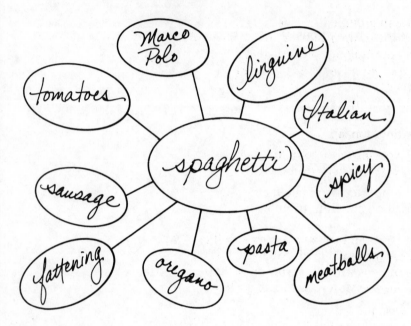

After using one or another of the above techniques, the students organize their random thoughts, and they are ready to write.

Step B.

Next, the teacher should review those particular writing and precomposing skills which the specific writing task calls for. Such precomposing skills may include reviewing a business letter format, a friendly letter format, the organization of a compare/contrast essay, the use of quotation marks, etc.

Step C.

The writing task should be as clear and precise as possible. The writing task should sound like a *prompt,* wherein all crucial information is given. Students should be able to read this prompt and know exactly what they are to write, without further guidance from the teacher.

Step D.

The next task is editing. Students must edit their own work, both alone and in small groups. Be sure that students have specific goals in editing. For example, has every requirement of the prompt been met? Is every word properly spelled? Are there complete sentences throughout? Are paragraphs well organized? Are there clear transitions?

Step E.

Finally, the teacher should evaluate the paper (unless he or she has already indicated that the papers would not be evaluated). The teacher may be as casual or as thorough as the task warrants. However, he or she must evaluate the paper strictly in accordance with the standards previously established in the class.

Random Thoughts

1. Whenever possible, students should write for real audiences—not just for the teacher. Don't have them write hypothetical letters. Have them write real ones, so that there may be a possibility of a real reply.
2. Never force students to participate in group editing or in "magic circles." Students have a right to their privacy, too.
3. A great way to begin a class: Have the students write five to ten minute essays about the home economics subject at hand. A variety of techniques or formats can be used, such as diaries, poems, descriptions, steps in a process, etc.

Sample Sequence to Teach Basic Writing Concepts

You may use the sequence below in working with your students. The sequence is unchangeable, but the details vary from task to task.

Prewriting Experience

Ask the students to look around the room and to list as many specific details, large and small, as they can. Share these by writing them on the board. Have students compose a one-sentence description of the room, choosing details from among those listed on the board if they wish.

Precomposing Skills

Collect the sentences and write some of them on the board without revealing the authors' names. Conduct a class discussion on which sentences most effectively create a word picture of the room. If any sentences are examples of run-ons or fragments, lead the class to an awareness of what constitutes a complete sentence.

Assignment

The teacher and the students visit a place on the campus such as the cafeteria, auditorium, agriculture area, etc. Tell the students that many details may be perceived by senses other than sight—touch, smell, taste, hearing. Upon return to the classroom, have the students write a one-sentence description of the area visited, using their notes for material.

Evaluation

Select examples from sentences and ditto them, without names. The following class period, pass out dittos and ask students to choose and comment on:

1. Which sentence describes the area most effectively? Why?
2. Which uses the most concrete detail? Cite evidence.
3. Is any sentence not a complete sentence? Which one? Point out the sentence error.

HOME ECONOMICS-BASED MATHEMATICS SKILLS

The mathematics continuum, upon which the activity objectives in this guide are based, is included to provide teachers with an overview of some of the tasks which must be performed by a student who can compute successfully. It should be pointed out that not all the secondary continuum is included because algebra, geometry, etc., are not practiced in consumer home economics courses.

Students have the most difficulty untangling word problems. Therefore, a list of "Computation Key Words" has been added to indicate to teachers what words students need to identify to successfully solve word problems.

The teacher-managed activities and the student worksheets in this guide include many types of word problems. The display/multiple choice types used are close in format to those found in proficiency tests. Other types of problems will provide an opportunity for students to work through typical everyday life situations, such as comparing the cost of eating at a restaurant to the cost of eating at home. The more practice students have in solving problems such as these, the more successful they will be in answering test questions and functioning in society.

Mathematics Continuum, Grades 7-12

Whole Numbers

Writes standard numerals in expanded notation, and vice versa.
Adds numbers, regrouping as necessary.
Subtracts numbers, regrouping as necessary.
Multiplies a number by a number, regrouping as necessary.
Divides a number by a number, with and without remainders.
Expresses the remainder of a division problem as a fraction.
Operates with zero, especially in division by zero.
Identifies the value represented by the digit in any place in any number less than ten million.

Fractions

Demonstrates understanding of the meaning of common fractions.
Changes fractions to lowest terms.
Performs the fundamental operations on common fractions.
Identifies and renames mixed numbers as improper fractions, and vice versa.
Performs the four fundamental operations on common fractions and mixed numbers.
Performs the four fundamental operations on whole numbers and fractions.
Uses the division algorithm for rational numbers.
Revises ratios to simpler form.

Determines which of two ratios is greater.
Solves a proportion.
Uses proportions to solve simple word problems.

Decimals

Identifies and expresses decimal place value.
Compares and orders decimals.
Changes fractions with denominators of some multiple of 10 to decimals.
Changes common fractions and mixed numbers to decimal form.
Performs the fundamental operations on decimal numbers.
Performs the fundamental operations on decimals and whole numbers.
Multiplies and divides decimals by some multiple of 10.
Understands the relationship between common and decimal fractions.
Rounds off numbers resulting from calculations.
Performs fundamental operations on rational numbers.

Percent

Changes hundredths fractions to percents, and vice versa.
Changes common fractions to equivalent common fractions with denominators of 100.
Changes common fractions to percents.
Relates percents to fractions or decimals.
Finds the percent of a number.
Finds what percent one number is of another.
Finds the whole when a percent of it is known.
Uses percents in simple applications.
Solves equations associated with percent problems.
Uses percents in practical situations.

Financial Transactions

Computes the number of hours worked.
Computes the hourly pay.
Computes the total pay for work during regular time.
Computes the difference in pay for two rates.
Computes the take-home pay.
Computes the taxable income.
Computes the property tax from the assessed valuation rate.
Computes all the income and charges in a business transaction to determine profit or loss.

Personal Finance

Makes a deposit and computes the balance.
Makes a deposit of coins, currency, and checks and finds the sum of the deposit.
Writes a check and computes the balance.
Writes several checks and computes the balance.
Checks the entries on a check register to determine whether they are accurate.
Computes the cost of an item from the amounts of the down payment and a given number of monthly payments.
Computes the cost of installment buying.
Plans reasonable budgets and keeps accurate records of expenditures.
Demonstrates understanding of the use of credit.
Makes calculations involving various taxes encountered in daily life.

Expenses

Computes the sum of several amounts of money.
Multiplies and divides an amount of money by a whole number.
Computes the amount of an order from a menu.
Computes the sales tax.
Computes the change to be received.
Computes average weekly expenses.
Computes the amount of an allowance remaining after expenses.
Computes the cost of an item after deducting two different taxes.
Computes the lowest cost per unit.
Computes the total cost of several units from the cost of one unit.
Computes the amount of discount.
Computes the cost of parking for a given number of hours.
Computes rental expense.
Makes calculations involved in owning a home/renting an apartment.

Applications

Makes up a real-life problem from a number sentence and solves the problem.
Writes and solves a number sentence to reflect a real-life situation.
Sketches diagrams from descriptions.
Estimates freely to test the reasonableness of answers.
Offers information illustrating the use of mathematics in everyday life.
Uses mathematics to organize an approach to problem solving.
Uses mathematics to judge consumer experiences.
Applies mathematics to the solution of consumer problems.
Evaluates calculations encountered in daily life.
Calculates the sums and differences of several quantities of money.
Performs the four fundamental operations in practical situations.
Visits community centers to study how the processes of mathematics are used.

Measurement

Computes linear measurements.
Computes area measurements.
Computes volumes of solids.
Computes mass measurements.
Reads thermometers.
Computes the difference in temperatures.
Computes the elapsed time in a given situation.
Computes the times at which medicine should be taken.
Computes the distance that a car will travel on a specific quantity of gas.
Computes the amount of paint needed.
Changes two different units of measurement to one unit.

Modifies recipes by increasing or decreasing the amount of ingredients to make desired quantities of food or drink.
Recalls relations among, and solves problems involving denominate numbers.
Estimates, measures, and determines the relationship between two quantities, using metric linear units.
Estimates and measures the size of an area to determine its relationship to another area, using metric area units.
Estimates and computes the volume of a given container, using metric units, to determine its relationship to the volume of a second container.
Estimates and measures capacity of a given container, using metric units, to determine its relationship to the capacity of a second container.
Estimates and measures the mass of a given object, using metric units, to determine its relationship to a second mass.
Estimates and measures temperature, using the Celsius scale.

COMPUTATION KEY WORDS

When the following words appear in a word problem, they may indicate that a specific arithmetical computation may need to be made.

- Area
- Average
- Border
- Deposit
- Discount
- Exclude
- Gross
- Including/not including
- Interest
- Net
- Perimeter
- Volume
- Withdraw

Pay Terms: Deductions, earnings, gross pay, income tax, net pay, overtime, payroll, rate of pay, regular pay, salary, time card, wages.

Tax Terms: Exemption, F.E.T., income tax (federal and state), sales tax, tax liability, withhold.

The mathematical key words herewith have been included to help teachers help students identify some of the processes that must be done in order to sort out the components of computation word problems. *Note:* The word *and, each,* or *per* in a word problem may be a clue or signal that more than one mathematical operation is needed to solve the problem.

Addition (+)

1. Total
2. Sum
3. All together
4. And
5. Deposit
6. _____ , _____ , and _____ : How much
7. Including

Subtraction (–)

1. Difference
2. How much warmer, cooler, bigger, smaller, shorter, taller?
3. How much is left? How much remains?
4. How much more?
5. How much less?
6. How much is refunded?
7. Withdraw
8. Write a check
9. Deduct
10. How much is saved?
11. How much change?

Multiplication (×)

1. You know the cost of 1: How much are 2, 3, 4, etc.
2. Each
3. Per
4. Double, triple, etc.

Division (÷)

1. Split
2. Each
3. Per
4. Half, third, etc.
5. Cut in half, etc.
6. How many are in. . . .

Special Functions

1. AVERAGE: add, then divide
2. GROSS: total of everything
3. NET: gross minus deductions
4. AREA: rectangle = length × width
5. PERIMETER, BORDER: add lengths of sides
6. ROUND OFF

FRACTIONS: A BULLETIN BOARD IDEA

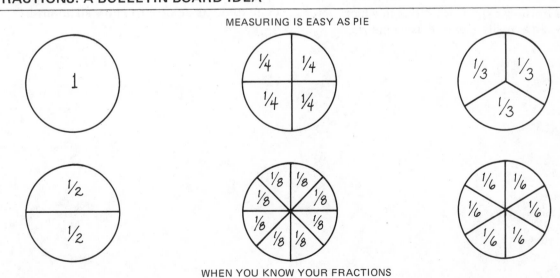

MEASURING IS EASY AS PIE

WHEN YOU KNOW YOUR FRACTIONS

SETTING STANDARDS FOR METRIC

An Interview with an Expert:
Gladys Earl, Certified Advanced Metric Specialist and member of the Food and Nutrition Department faculty, School of Home Economics at University of Wisconsin–Stout.

Is metric ever going to make it in this country?

Of course. In fact, as our students learn the metric system, they become our greatest proponents. Today they are completely sold on the metric system and request that classes be taught metrically.

Why do they enjoy metric so much?

That's simple . . . it's simple.

The metric system is an easy language to learn and a convenient one to use. Because it's based on multiples of ten, or the decimal system, it's easy to remember and quick for calculations.

As an example, it's a cinch to increase or decrease quantities in recipes or adjust patterns using metric.

Yes, but you work with college students. Do you think high school students can adapt to metric as well?

I've been involved with metric for more than ten years and serve as a U.S. Metric Association regional director and a member of the American National Metric Council. Through all these activities, I've worked with people of all ages and I can tell you, people really do like metric once they know what it's about and how it can be useful to them.

I frankly think metric would be much more sensible for students in high school today than conventional measurements because metric is the measuring language of the future.

How do you introduce metric to students?

The best learning experience is one in which students can actually measure using metric.

I suggest that educators use posters or other visuals and introduce one unit at a time. For example, I might have a food-preparation lesson on combining liquids, perhaps making pudding measuring milliliters and liters.

Another day, I might focus on length—have a home-decorating lesson on measuring curtains or draperies in centimeters and meters.

One thing is critical: If the educator follows the established guidelines and SI standards (International System of Units), this will help eliminate confusion.

Can you give a quick overview of the typical metric measurements that a student should learn first?

Volume. Small amounts are measured in milliliters (ml.). Since the prefix "milli" means "thousand," there are a thousand milliliters in a liter (L). A liter is slightly more than a quart in our conventional system.

Weight. The gram (g) is used for small amounts. The kilogram (kg), which is slightly over two pounds, is used to measure larger amounts such as body weights.

Length. The centimeter (cm) is a small unit of measure. Two and a half centimeters are equal to one inch. The meter (m) is slightly longer than a yard.

Temperature. The unit of measure is degree Celsius (C).

What advice would you give educators who are interested in adding more metric emphasis to their curriculum?

I'd say, start right now. Metric is becoming the universal language among leaders in government, business, industry, and education.

The metric system is precise and practical. Your students deserve to know all about it!

PART II

TEACHER AND STUDENT MANAGED ACTIVITIES IN READING, WRITING, AND MATHEMATICS

FOODS AND NUTRITION
Teacher-Managed Reading Activities

BUILDING VOCABULARY

1. Q-Sort

Make a "Q-Sort" by dividing an 8½" x 11" page into 16 sections. Write one word per section. Copy one page per student and cut apart. Students then sort into various types of stacks, depending upon the subject matter. Categories for foods classes could be:

- Foods I Like
- Foods I Dislike
- Foods I've Never Tasted

The more words, the more interesting the ensuing discussion! Have the students store each set in an envelope.

2. Applying Vocabulary Knowledge

After students know and/or have written the definitions of the words from their vocabulary lists, have them use the words in sentences.

3. Homonyms

Homonyms are two or more words spelled and pronounced alike, but they *differ in meaning.* Have students think of homonyms related to the area of foods and nutrition, e.g., bouillon, cobbler, ice, dough, roll, etc.

4. Words via Borrowing

Words enter the English language in many ways. Probably the most frequent way in which words have become part of the English language is *via borrowing.* Have students appreciate the origin of the following food and dining words:

a la mode	crème	fondue
al dente	crepe	glace
aspic	demitasse	hors d'oeuvre
au gratin	eclair	legumes
au jus	en brochette	potage
canapé	entrée	ragout

5. Using Abbreviations

Have students recognize and use commonly used abbreviations in recipes, e.g., T., Tbsp., t., tsp., pt., qt.

IMPROVING COMPREHENSION

1. Summarizing

Have students summarize information that they have read in the newspaper relating to nutrition. (*Literal Comprehension*)

2. Diet Information

Have students read about various diet plans and answer the following questions: who, what, which, when, where, why, and how? (*Literal Comprehension*)

3. Cause and Effect

Have students identify cause and effect relationships in the following situations:

- eating every day in a fast food restaurant
- trying different fad diets
- preparing a gourmet meal in a hurry

(*Inferential Comprehension*)

4. Applying Logic

Have students determine the most logical thing to do in a number of different situations:

- grease fire in the kitchen
- unexpected people arrive at your house for dinner
- you're on a diet and your friends invite you to a make-your-own-sundae party

Read one another's comments.
(*Applicative Comprehension*)

5. Analyzing

(Refer to Appendix 14.) Analyze advertisements of food and health products to determine the propaganda technique being used. (*Analytical Comprehension*)

LOCATION-STUDY SKILLS

Plan exercises to give students practice in locating information in or on:

- cookbook index pages
- recipe analysis
- newspaper—food section
- magazines—health and beauty ads

Teacher-Managed Writing Activities

JOURNAL WRITING
(Refer to Appendix 1.)

Use words that employ the five senses and use the following topics
as journal entries:

- After eating certain foods, I . . .
- I would like to change my eating habits . . .
- In a grocery store, I . . .
- Nutrition means . . .

FILMSTRIP WRITING
(Refer to Appendixes 2–4.)

Choose vocabulary appropriate for the mode/audience:

- Nutritious snacks for children (geared for toddlers)
- Kitchen safety
- Fad diets

LETTER TO THE EDITOR
(Refer to Appendix 5.)

Write an editorial for the community paper using one of the
following topics:

- Editorial about junk food, fast food, or food additives
- Review of a local restaurant or health food bar
- Hidden sugar (or salt) in foods

CONSUMER BUSINESS LETTER
(Refer to Appendixes 6–8.)

1. Write a letter of complaint to a manufacturer expressing
   displeasure with a food product; be specific.
2. Write a letter requesting better labeling procedures for a
   particular product.

WRITING LISTS
(Refer to Appendix 13.)

1. List the steps in preparing a simple-to-prepare food. Include
   ingredients, size of pan, temperature, etc.
2. List the steps in planning a low-calorie reducing diet.

FOODS AND NUTRITION

Unit Vocabulary List

The following sample vocabulary list demonstrates the use of *unit vocabulary* for a 20-week Consumer Foods class. Preparation of 20-week unit plans should involve vocabulary development related to weekly lessons. Some of these words appear on the Foods and Nutrition Vocabulary List.

List 1
homemaking
equipment
electricity
refrigerator
appliance
disposal
silverware
utensils
container
hazard

List 2
breakfast
blender
laundry
detergent
nutrition
carbohydrates
vitamins
protein
demonstration

List 3
cooperation
schedule
directions
recipe
management
preparation
poached
scrambled
omelet
soufflé

List 4
measure
estimate
cereal
cookery
skillet
griddle
leavening agent
enriched
accurate

List 5
well-planned
essential
allowance
moderate
recommended
appetite
attractive
etiquette
menu
nutrients

List 6
ingredients
technique
knead
proportion
substitute
lightness
tenderness
granulated
refined
cinnamon

List 7
luncheon
hostess
guest
buffet
brunch
individual
evaluate
variations
white sauce
thickener

List 8
casserole
macaroni
spaghetti
noodle
pasta
versatile
seasoning
economical
au gratin

List 9
lettuce
endive
roughage
cucumber
tomato
romaine
escarole
scallion
garnish
tossed salad

List 10
pastry
flaky
cobbler
turnovers
chiffon
glaze
pumpkin
meringue
graham cracker
pudding

List 11
sponge
cupcakes
frosting
texture
creamed
shortening
minimum
alternately
delicate
layer

List 12
soggy
volume
imprint
decorated
molded
chilling
aluminum
chocolate

List 13
tradition
holiday
centerpiece
appetizers
carafe
flatware
porcelain
china
plastic

List 14
inspection
principles
wholesale
retail
moist
tenderized
roasting
broil
braise
aroma

List 15
thermometer
hamburger
sandwiches
chuck
flank
brisket
loin
pork
poultry

List 16
stewing
shrimp
oysters
tuna
scallops
halibut
perch
salmon
lobster
shellfish

FOODS AND NUTRITION

Vocabulary List

accident
advertising
a la carte
appliance

bake
balanced
barbecue
baste
braise
breakfast
broil
broiler
butter

calories
candles
carbohydrates
caramelize
casserole
centerpiece
cereal
cheese
chocolate
cinnamon
citrus
compare
consumer
cookies
cooperation
cube

dice
diet
directions
discount
dissolve
dough
dredge

electric
equipment
etiquette
evaluate

fats
fish
flour
fraud
fricassee
fruit

gas
goblet
graduated spoons
grate
grater
griddle
grill
grind
grocery

hamburger
hazard

ingredients

knead
knives

labels
ladder
lard
linens
liquid

margarine
marinate
measure
meat
microwave
mince
mineral
mixer

napkin
nutrient
nutrition

omelet
ounce (oz.)
outlet

peel
place mat
planning
poultry
pound (lb.)
protein

recipe
refrigerator
render
rotary beater

safety
sanitation
saucepan
sauté
scald
sear
shopping
shortening
sifter
silverware
slice
snacks
snip
spatula
specials
steep
sterilize
stew
stir

tablespoon (tbsp., T.)
teaspoon (tsp., t.)
temperature
timer
tortilla
tostada

utensils

vanilla
vegetable
vitamin

whip
wire whisk

yolk

FOODS AND NUTRITION

Student Worksheets—Teaching Strategies

The answers for the Foods and Nutrition student worksheets are found in the Answer Key, p. 227. Teaching strategies for selected student worksheets are found below.

COMPARISON OF FOOD PRICES

This lesson has two purposes:

1. Students learn to read the food specials in the newspapers.
2. Students practice finding and comparing prices of foods.

Materials Needed

1. One copy of the student worksheet for each student.
2. Store advertisements from the Food section of newspapers.
   (Note: Dates do not need to be current, just recent.)

An Alternate Assignment

Students can take their worksheets to a grocery store and find out current prices. Junior high students might go to a store with adults, if there is no store within walking distance.

Initial Lesson

Students practice reading advertisements. They should know the names of the stores, how to find brand names and sizes, and how to determine whether a price is regular or special.

An overhead transparency, made from the student worksheet, would be an aid in showing students how to complete the assignment.

SNACK FOOD ANALYSIS

This exercise is designed to help students learn how to read labels. In addition, students will learn how to calculate nutrient density. Nutrient density is a score which shows how high in nutrients a food is in relationship to its calorie content. It is calculated by a simple formula. (It is *most easily* calculated when the nutrients and percentage of recommended daily dietary allowance are listed on the label.)

Formula for Nutrient Density

1. Add the total percentages of RDAs for eight nutrients—protein, Vitamin A, Vitamin C, Thiamine, Riboflavin, Niacin, Calcium, and Iron.
2. Divide this total by the number of calories.
3. Multiply by 100, to get the number for 100 grams.

4. The score is the nutrient density. 32 is considered the dividing line. If a food has a score *under* 32, it is a low-nutrient-density food. If *over* 32, it is a high-density food. Broccoli has a score of almost 1,000, making it an extremely high-nutrient-density food!

Activities

Read the nutrients from a variety of food labels. As a class, practice calculating the nutrient density formula. Give the students the worksheets. You or they can provide a variety of labels to use. Have them figure out the scores. Discuss results!

Foods and Nutrition

Objective: Recognize and use dictionary entry word information. **(Reading)**

A COOKING DICTIONARY

Directions: Read the terms and definitions. Then circle the letter of the best answer in each question.

---

bake (bāk) v. baked, baking, bakes. (1) to cook (bread, pastry, or other food) with continuous, even, dry heat especially in an oven. (2) to harden, dry.

baste (bāst) v. basted, basting, bastes. To pour pan drippings or sauce over (meat) while cooking.

blend (blend), v.t. blended or blent, blending. To mix or mingle varieties of (tea, spices, etc.) to mix thoroughly, to shade gradually into each other as color.

boil (boil) v.i. (L. bulla, a bubble). To bubble up and vaporize over direct heat. To be agitated, as with rage.

braise (brāz) v.t. braised, braising (Fr. braiser, live coals). To brown (meat) and then simmer slowly in a covered pan.

broil (broil) v. to cook by direct heat as over or under an electric coil; to expose to great heat.

---

1. What part of speech is given for the entry word *braise*?

   a. verb

   b. noun

   c. adverb

   d. adjective

2. On this page of the dictionary, which word would come immediately after the word *broil*?

   a. broth

   b. brown gravy

   c. broccoli

   d. brownie

3. What definition of the word *blend* would be appropriate for foods?

   a. to heat

   b. to mix

   c. to bake

   d. to whip

4. What is the best method of preparing meat that needs a long time to cook?

   a. braise

   b. baste

   c. bake

   d. broil

Foods and Nutrition

Name   Date   Period   Score

Objective: Follow written directions to complete specific tasks. **(Reading)**

READING AND UNDERSTANDING DIRECTIONS

Yellow Cake Mix

Preheat Preheat oven to 350°. Generously grease (about 1/2 Tablespoon each pan) and then flour pans.

Mix In large bowl combine mix, 1-1/3 cups of water and 2 eggs; blend until moistened. Beat 2 minutes at medium speed. If hand mixing, beat vigorously 300 strokes.

Bake Bake at 350° until done. Cake is done if toothpick inserted in center comes out clean. Do **not** test for doneness by touching with finger.

Two 8" x 1-1/2" round layers	about 30-35 minutes
Two 9" x 1-1/2" round layers	about 25-30 minutes
One 13" x 9" x 2" oblong	about 30-35 minutes
One tube pan, 10" or fluted	about 35-45 minutes
24 medium cup cakes	about 15-20 minutes

Cool Cool 10 to 20 minutes in pan (for tube pan cool 25 minutes). Remove from pan and cool top side up. Frost when fully cool. See side panel for frosting recipe.

When baking at high altitude or using only 1/2 package, see side panel.

Directions: Underline the best answer in the following questions.

1. John's cake pan is 13" x 9" x 2" oblong. Approximately how long will he bake the cake?

   a. 30 to 35 minutes
   b. 15 to 20 minutes
   c. 35 to 45 minutes
   d. 25 to 30 minutes

2. How much water will John need for the mix?

   a. 1½ cup
   b. 1 cup
   c. ⅓ cup
   d. 1⅓ cup

3. At what temperature should John set the oven?

   a. 325 degrees
   b. 350 degrees
   c. 400 degrees
   d. 300 degrees

4. John will need the following ingredients:

   a. eggs and milk
   b. eggs, grease, flour
   c. eggs, water
   d. grease, flour, eggs, and water

5. John will need to cool the cake in the pan for:

   a. 10–20 minutes
   b. 25 minutes

6. If John will be frosting the cake, he can frost it:

   a. just out of the oven
   b. after 20 minutes
   c. after one or more hours
   d. when fully cooled off

Foods and Nutrition

Name _____ Date _____ Period _____ Score _____

Objective: Use appropriate reference materials. **(Reading)**

LEARNING TO MEASURE

Directions: Using a class textbook, study the instructions for measuring ingredients when cooking. Complete the statements below.

1. When measuring brown sugar, be sure to _____ it down to get an accurate amount.

2. To measure granulated sugar, use a cup designed for

    _____ ingredients.

3. Liquid ingredients should be measured in a _____ cup.

4. Before measuring flour, it should be _____ to get an accurate measurement.

5. If you need a ⅛ tsp. measurement, you would use a ¼ tsp. and

    _____ by half.

6. There are _____ tsps. in 1 tablespoon.

7. There are _____ tablespoons in 1 cup.

8. If the correct measuring cup is not available, you can measure solid shortening by using a liquid measuring cup and the

    _____ method.

Extra Activity

1. Demonstrate to the class one method of measuring flour, brown sugar, liquids, solid shortening, salt, or spices.

2. Write a step-by-step instruction describing the method of measuring that you used for your choice. Exchange your work with a partner and have him/her determine if the instructions are accurate.

Foods and Nutrition

Name _____ Date _____ Period _____ Score _____

Objective: Interpret labels to identify relevant information. **(Reading)**

ANALYZING LABELS FOR INFORMATION

Directions: Read the labels below. Use the information to answer the following questions.

BLUEBERRY MUFFIN MIX

NUTRITION INFORMATION PER PORTION

PORTION SIZE...1/12 PKG.
PORTIONS PER PKG.....12

	1/12 pkg. + 1/12 whole egg +	1/12 pkg. 2 tsp. milk
CALORIES.. 100	120	
PROTEIN, g. 1	2	
CARBOHY-DRATE, g. 18	19	
FAT, g. 3	4	
SODIUM, mg 145	155	

(450 mg/100 g mix)

PERCENTAGE OF U.S. RECOMMENDED DAILY ALLOWANCES (U.S. RDA)

PROTEIN...	2	4
VITAMIN A..	*	*
VITAMIN C..	*	*
THIAMIN ...	4	4
RIBOFLAVIN	2	4
NIACIN	2	2
CALCIUM ..	2	4
IRON	2	2

*CONTAINS LESS THAN 2 PERCENT OF THE U.S. RDA OF THESE NUTRIENTS.

INGREDIENTS

ENRICHED FLOUR BLEACHED [WHEAT FLOUR, MALTED BARLEY FLOUR, NIACIN (A B VITAMIN), IRON, THIAMIN MONONITRATE (VITAMIN B₁), RIBOFLAVIN (VITAMIN B₂)], BLUEBERRIES CANNED IN WATER, SUGAR, ANIMAL AND/OR VEGETABLE SHORTENING (CONTAINS ONE OR MORE OF THE FOLLOWING PARTIALLY HYDROGENATED FATS: SOYBEAN OIL, COTTONSEED OIL, BEEF TALLOW, PALM OIL; AND/OR LARD) WITH FRESHNESS PRESERVED BY BHA AND BHT; DEXTROSE, LEAVENING (BAKING SODA, SODIUM ALUMINUM PHOSPHATE, MONOCALCIUM PHOSPHATE), MODIFIED CORN STARCH, SALT, WHEAT STARCH, ARTIFICIAL FLAVOR.

PINEAPPLE SLICES

INGREDIENTS: PINEAPPLE AND PINEAPPLE JUICE

NUTRITION INFORMATION PER SERVING
SERVING SIZE .....1 CUP (4 SLICES AND JUICE)
SERVING PER CONTAINER 2 1/2

CALORIES 140	CARBOHYDRATES ..35 GRAMS
PROTEIN.........1 GRAM	FAT ....1 GRAM

PERCENTAGE OF U.S. RECOMMENDED DAILY ALLOWANCES (U.S. RDA) OF PROTEIN, VITAMINS, AND MINERALS PER 1 CUP SERVING:

PROTEIN ....*	RIBOFLAVIN 2
VITAMIN A 2	NIACIN 2
VITAMIN C 10	CALCIUM 2
THIAMINE 10	IRON 4

*CONTAINS LESS THAN 2 PERCENT OF THE U.S. RDA OF THESE NUTRIENTS

DISTRIBUTED BY © ACME STORES INCORPORATED
HEAD OFFICE: DUBUQUE, IOWA 52001

‡WT. OF PINEAPPLE (14 OZ.) BEFORE ADDITION OF LIQUID NECESSARY FOR PROCESSING

Sample:

How many grams of carbohydrate are there in 1 cup of pineapple slices and juice?

Answer:

35 grams

---

1. How much fat is in one blueberry muffin? _____ g

2. How many calories are there in 1 cup of pineapple slices? _____

3. Which ingredient is found in greatest quantity in the mix? _____

4. What two nutrients are less than 2% of the U.S. RDA in the muffin mix?
   a. _____
   b. _____

5. What was the weight of the pineapple before adding liquid? _____ oz

6. Where is the head office of ACME stores located? _____

7. What two ingredients preserve freshness in the muffin mix? _____

8. How many servings are there in one can of pineapple slices? _____

9. What is the scientific name of vitamin B1? _____

Foods and Nutrition

Objectives: Use appropriate reference materials to gather information; compute the cost per unit. **(Reading; Math)**

COMPARISON OF FOOD PRICES

Directions: Read the store advertisements in the weekly food section of the newspaper. Find the ads from two major supermarkets. Fill in the specific name of the item in the first column. Fill in the brand name listed in the ad, as well as the size and price. If an item is not listed, write N/A in the Brand Name space.

STORE #1 _____

TYPE OF ITEM	SPECIFIC ITEM	BRAND NAME	SIZE/ WEIGHT	PRICE	UNIT PRICE
CANNED VEGETABLE				$.	$ ./
FROZEN VEGETABLE				.	./
FRESH VEGETABLE				.	./
FRESH FRUIT		– – – – – –		.	./
WHITE BREAD	– – – – – –			.	./
WHOLE WHEAT BREAD	– – – – – –			.	./
DAIRY PRODUCT				.	./
GROUND MEAT				.	./
CHICKEN, WHOLE, CUT-UP				.	./
1 DOZ. EGGS	– – – – – –			.	./

STORE #2 _____

TYPE OF ITEM	SPECIFIC ITEM	BRAND NAME	SIZE/ WEIGHT	PRICE	UNIT PRICE
CANNED VEGETABLE				$.	$ ./
FROZEN VEGETABLE				.	./
FRESH VEGETABLE				.	./
FRESH FRUIT		– – – – – –		.	./
WHITE BREAD	– – – – – –			.	./
WHOLE WHEAT BREAD	– – – – – –			.	./
DAIRY PRODUCT				.	./
GROUND MEAT				.	./
CHICKEN, WHOLE, CUT-UP				.	./
1 DOZ. EGGS	– – – – – –			.	./

Foods and Nutrition

Objectives: Use appropriate reference materials to gather information; do simple computations. **(Reading; Math)**

SNACK FOOD ANALYSIS

Directions: Some snack food labels show the number of calories in the snack foods and the percentage of RDA (Recommended Daily Allowance) that the snack foods provide. You may use the Nutrient Density Formula to find out how high in nutrients a food is in relationship to its calorie content.

Find a variety of foods to analyze, such as candy, cookies, and chips. The Nutrient Density Formula is as follows: Add up all the percents of RDAs for a snack food. Divide by the number of calories. Then multiply by 100 to get the Nutrient Density Score for that food.

ITEM/BRAND	A	B	C	D	E	F	G	H
1. CALORIES								
2. PROTEIN								
3. VITAMIN A								
4. VITAMIN C								
5. THIAMINE								
6. RIBOFLAVIN								
7. NIACIN								
8. CALCIUM								
9. IRON								
TOTALS								
NUTRIENT DENSITY SCORE								

(Rows 2–9 are grouped under the label PERCENTAGE OF RDA)

Foods and Nutrition

Foods and Nutrition

Name _____ Date _____ Period _____ Score _____

Objective: Write anecdotes of personal experiences. **(Writing)**

THE APPEAL OF FOODS

Discuss some of your eating habits!

Directions: *In the first paragraph,* describe several foods you like best. *In the second paragraph,* describe several foods you dislike. *In the third paragraph,* describe some of the reasons why you like or dislike particular foods. (Example: Sometimes as a child you were forced to eat a particular food, or clean your plate.) Use complete sentences, and correct spelling and punctuation.

Foods I like best:

_____

_____

_____

_____

_____

Foods I dislike:

_____

_____

_____

_____

Why I like and/or dislike particular foods:

_____

_____

_____

_____

Foods and Nutrition

Objective: Organic information for a specific purpose. **(Writing)**

MENU PLANNING FROM THE NEWSPAPER

Directions: Read the store advertisements in the weekly food section of the newspaper. Be particularly aware of specials for the week, marking those you might purchase.

Plan a menu for your family for three days, using as many of the specials as possible. Include three meals and snacks, making sure you include the Basic Four Plus One (Basic Five) food groups daily. Mark all specials in your menus with a star. Write a shopping list for foods you will need to buy.

	DAY 1	DAY 2	DAY 3
BREAKFAST			
LUNCH			
DINNER			
SNACK FOOD			

Did you include the Basic Four Plus One (Basic Five) Food Groups each day?

_____ Yes   _____ No

If no, what group(s) do you need to add?

_____ Meat, poultry, fish, and eggs   _____ Milk and dairy products

_____ Fruits and vegetables   _____ Bread and cereals

          _____ Sweets, fats, and oils*

*Remember, use much less of these than the foods in the other food groups.

Foods and Nutrition

Name   Date   Period   Score

Objectives: Write a comparison among similar products; compute the cost per unit.
(Writing; Math)

COMPARING CANNED FOODS

Directions: Compare three different brands of canned foods, such
as peas or green beans. Record the information requested on the
chart below.

FOOD _____

BRAND	COST	NET WEIGHT		COST PER	
		OZS.	GRAMS	OZ.	GRAM

In the space below, write a paragraph describing why you would buy
one brand instead of the other two. (Remember, it is good to buy for
a thrifty price, but quality must be considered, too. You would have
to look at the canned vegetables themselves for appearance, color, and
uniformity.)

_____

_____

_____

_____

Foods and Nutrition

Name _____ Date _____ Period _____ Score _____

Objective: Use metric units to measure the capacity of containers. **(Math)**

MAKING METRIC PUNCH

Fruit Punch Recipe

Combine the following ingredients in a punch bowl.

> 597 ml of water
> 60 ml of frozen lemonade (concentrate, defrosted)
> 45 ml of fruit punch (concentrate, bottled)
> <u>298</u> ml of orange juice (fresh or reconstituted)

Total _____ ml

1. If your punch bowl holds 1,250 ml, how many milliliters will
   you have on the top of the punch for an ice ring and/or
   decorations?

   _____ ml

CUP A   CUP B

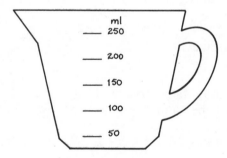   

2. Which ingredients can you measure in cup A, without
   dividing up any ingredients and measuring twice?

   _____ AND _____

3. For which ingredients do you need to use cup B,
   without dividing up and measuring twice?

   _____ AND _____

4. How many milliliters are represented by each small
   division of

   Cup A _____ ml   Cup B _____ ml

Foods and Nutrition

Name   Date   Period   Score

Objective: Use metric units to measure mass. **(Math)**

METRIC WEIGHT AT THE GROCERY STORE

Directions: The following items have been purchased at the supermarket.
Their weight is labeled in metric units. Complete the problems below,
giving answers in metric units. Circle the best answer to each question.

Item	Weight
1 box of crackers	340 grams
Salad seasoning	62 grams
Non-dairy creamer	170 grams
Instant coffee	280 grams

1. If 2 boxes of crackers are
   purchased, the total weight
   in grams will be

   a. 430 grams

   b. 680 grams

   c. 780 grams

2. If half of the jar of instant
   coffee is used in 1 week, how
   many grams will be left?

   a. 120 grams

   b. 140 grams

   c. 160 grams

3. The non-dairy creamer is
   used at the rate of 2 grams
   per day. How many days will
   it last?

   a. 85 days

   b. 160 days

   c. 170 days

4. What is the total metric
   weight of the 4 purchases?

   a. 652 grams

   b. 752 grams

   c. 852 grams

Foods and Nutrition

Name _____ Date _____ Period _____ Score _____

Objectives: Acquire a facility in using metric and customary units;
draw conclusions. **(Math; Writing)**

USING METRIC AND CUSTOMARY UNITS

Directions: Complete the following problems in customary units
and metric units.

AREA

1. What is the *area* of the floor of a room with the following dimensions?

Customary Units

Length	15 ft.	7 in.
Width	12 ft.	6 in.

Answer _____ sq. ft. _____ sq. in. _____

Metric Units

475 centimeters
380 centimeters

Answer _____ sq. cm _____

WEIGHT

2. What is the approximate total weight of the contents of a grocery
basket with the following items?

Customary Units

Meat	4 lbs.	9 oz.
Potatoes	3 lbs.	4 oz.
Tomatoes	2 lbs.	15 oz.
Cereal	1 lb.	7 oz.

Answer _____ lb. _____ oz. _____

Metric Units

2.07 kilograms
1.47 kilograms
1.33 kilograms
650 grams

Answer _____ kg _____ g

VOLUME

3. What is the volume of each of the following two mixtures?

Customary Units

Milk	1 gal.	2 qt.	1 pt.
Water		3 qt.	1 pt.
Flavoring			½ pt.

Answer _____ gal. _____ qt. _____ pt. _____

Metric Units

6.5 liters
3.5 liters
250 milliliters

Answer _____ liters _____ milliliters

4. Which measuring system is easier to use, metric or customary? Why?

_____

_____

_____

Foods and Nutrition

Name   Date   Period   Score

Objective: Modify recipes by increasing or decreasing the amounts of ingredients. **(Math)**

RECIPE MATH

There are times when changes must be made in a recipe to alter the number of servings that can be made.

> *To double a recipe: multiply by 2*
>
> 1 cup flour $\times$ 2 = 2 cups flour
>
> *To cut a recipe in half: divide by 2*
>
> 1 cup flour $\div$ 2 = ½ cup flour

Directions: Practice doubling and dividing in half the following ingredients, using the real thing when possible.

CHEESECAKE INGREDIENTS	DOUBLED QUANTITY	CUT-IN-HALF QUANTITY
1. 5 pkg. cream cheese	Pkg.	Pkg.
2. 3 T flour	T.	T.
3. 4 eggs	Eggs	Eggs
4. ½ c. milk	Cup	Cup
5. ¼ tsp. vanilla	Tsp.	Tsp.
6. 1¾ c. sugar	Cup	Cup T.
7. 1½ tsp. soda	Tsp.	Tsp.

SPINACH LOAF INGREDIENTS	DOUBLED QUANTITY	CUT-IN-HALF QUANTITY
1. ¾ lb. ground beef	lb.	lb.
2. 1 bunch spinach	bunch	bunch
3. 1 small onion	onion	onion
4. 2 eggs	eggs	egg
5. 2 T flour	T	T
6. 1 T butter	T	T
7. ½ c. milk	cup	cup

Foods and Nutrition

Name   Date   Period   Score

Objective: Use mathematics to organize an approach to problem solving. **(Math)**

RECONSTITUTING MILK

Directions: Mary has a pudding recipe which requires 3 cups of milk. She has no whole milk and must use dry milk or evaporated milk. Study the facts and select the correct amounts she must prepare for her recipe. Circle the best answer.

EVAPORATED MILK	NONFAT DRY MILK
– – – – –	– – – – –
12 ounce can	Add ¾ cup water to ¼ cup dry milk = 1 cup reconstituted milk

1. To prepare evaporated milk for use, one must add an equal amount of water to the milk. If Mary does this, how many ounces of milk and water combined will she have from one 12 oz. can?

   a. 24 oz.

   b. 18 oz.

   c. 36 oz.

2. How many 8 oz. cups of evaporated milk and water combined will she have from one 12 oz. can?

   a. 4 cups

   b. 2½ cups

   c. 3 cups

3. How much dry milk will Mary need to use to get 3 cups of reconstituted milk?

   a. ¾ cup

   b. ½ cup

   c. 1 cup

4. How many cups of water must Mary use to get 3 cups of reconstituted milk, using dry milk?

   a. 1¼ cups

   b. 2¼ cups

   c. 2¾ cups

Foods and Nutrition

Objective: Modify recipes by increasing or decreasing the amounts of ingredients. **(Math)**

Directions: Study the following recipe and use the information to answer the following questions. Circle the correct answers.

MRS. ROSEN'S SUGAR COOKIES

Preheat oven to 400°

$\frac{2}{3}$ cup shortening	1 tsp. vanilla
$\frac{1}{2}$ cup sugar	1 tsp. baking powder
$\frac{1}{4}$ cup honey	1 tsp. salt
2 eggs	$2\frac{1}{4}$ cups whole wheat flour

1. Mix shortening, sugar, honey, eggs, and vanilla.
2. Stir in remaining ingredients.
3. Drop by teaspoon on ungreased baking sheet.
4. Bake 8–10 minutes or until light brown. Immediately remove from baking sheet.

Makes 3 dozen cookies.

1. How much flour is needed if this recipe is doubled?

   a. $1\frac{1}{2}$ cups

   b. $4\frac{1}{2}$ cups

   c. $2\frac{1}{2}$ cups

   d. $4\frac{1}{8}$ cups

2. Mrs. Rosen has been asked to make 12 dozen cookies. By what number will she need to multiply the recipe to make 12 dozen cookies?

   a. 12

   b. 9

   c. 4

   d. 6

3. How much shortening will be needed to double this recipe?

   a. $\frac{4}{6}$ cup

   b. $1\frac{1}{3}$ cup

   c. $\frac{1}{3}$ cup

   d. $1\frac{2}{3}$ cups

4. Mrs. Rosen's daughter wants to make 1½ dozen cookies. What should she do?

   a. double this recipe

   b. triple this recipe

   c. divide this recipe by two

Foods and Nutrition

Name   Date   Period   Score

Objectives: Find what percent one number is of another; write a short analysis of a problem. **(Math; Writing)**

PLANNING A FAMILY FOOD BUDGET

The Johnson family, which includes two adults, two young children, and one medium-sized dog, has a weekly take-home pay of $300. This family has many expenses, so they want to control their spending, especially for food. The U.S. Department of Agriculture suggests that families spend no more than 25% of their take-home pay on food, to be sure that other expenses are covered. As prices for food rise, the Johnsons are having a harder and harder time staying within their food budget. This 25% does not include personal items, frequently purchased at the grocery store.

    Directions: Please answer the following questions in the spaces provided.

1. If the Johnsons want to keep their food budget within 25% of take-home pay, what should be the maximum amount spent each week?

        $_____

2. This week the family spent the following amounts at the grocery store in the five food categories. It was the amount they could spend on food each week (25% of $300). Calculate the percentages in each group and the total spent on all items. Answer in the spaces provided. What percent of the total are each of the five food groups?

FOOD GROUP	COST	PERCENTAGE
MEAT, POULTRY, FISH, EGGS	$25.00	%
BREADS AND CEREALS	12.00	%
DAIRY PRODUCTS	15.00	%
FRUITS AND VEGETABLES	11.00	%
SWEETS, JAM, PICKLES, ETC.	12.00	%

                                                             Total $_____   100% (Approximately)

3. Last week the Johnsons spent $82.00 on groceries because they had guests for dinner. How many dollars did they overbuy on last week's budget?

        $_____

4. What suggestions do you have for reducing food bills for a family?

_____

On what foods would you personally be inclined to spend a large portion of your budget?

_____

Foods and Nutrition

Name _____ Date _____ Period _____ Score _____

Objective: Compute the lowest cost per unit. **(Math)**

ORANGE JUICE COMPARISON

Directions: A family is trying to determine the most economical way to purchase orange juice. The store in which they shop has frozen orange juice and fresh orange juice. Study the chart below and circle the best answer for each question.

> *Frozen orange juice*
> 6 oz. concentrate
> 78 cents per can

> *Fresh orange juice*
> 1 quart
> $1.60 per quart

1. What is the cost per ounce of a container of frozen juice before diluting?

   a. $ .13

   b.   .78

   c.   .60

2. One can of frozen orange juice concentrate, with the addition of 3 cans of water, will give how many ounces of juice?

   a. 40 oz.

   b. 24 oz.

   c. 32 oz.

3. What is the cost per ounce of the frozen juice when it has been diluted?

   a. $ .025

   b.   .033

   c.   .016

4. One quart of fresh orange juice costs $1.60. Thus the cost per ounce is

   a. $ .05

   b.   .15

   c.   .06

5. What is the difference in cost per ounce of the 2 types of juice?

   a. Approximately $ .035

   b. Approximately   .017

   c. Approximately   .002

6. Which juice is the least expensive per ounce? Check one.

   a. _____ fresh

   b. _____ frozen

Foods and Nutrition

Name   Date   Period   Score

Objectives: Perform the fundamental operations on decimal numbers; write a short paragraph of personal opinion. **(Math, Writing)**

FIGURING UNIT PRICING

Directions: Answer the following questions on the chart below:

1. Calculate the price per ounce of each of the large packages.
   (*Hint:* Divide price by ounces; watch the decimal point!)
2. Calculate the price per ounce of each of the small packages.
   (*Hint:* Use 1.5 instead of 1½ oz.)
3. Star the size which is least expensive in each category, either a or b.

ITEM	CONTAINER SIZE	COST	PRICE PER OUNCE	STAR BEST BUYS
1. RAISINS	15 oz.	$ .75	a. $.	
	1½ oz.	.10	b. .	
2. TOMATO JUICE	32 oz.	.89	a. .	
	12 oz.	.49	b. .	
3. RICE CEREAL	10 oz.	1.30	a. .	
	14 oz.	1.69	b. .	
4. PEANUT BUTTER	8 oz.	1.09	a. .	
	32 oz.	2.79	b. .	
5. CORN OIL	16 oz.	.91	a. .	
	32 oz.	1.65	b. .	

Note: Round off answers two places to right of decimal point.

4. Why is it important to calculate the cost per ounce, or use unit-pricing at the grocery store?

_____

_____

_____

_____

_____

Foods and Nutrition

Objective: Illustrate the use of mathemetics in everyday life. **(Math)**

COMPARISON SHOPPING

Pat wanted to find the lowest food prices in the city. She compared the prices of several foods at three stores. Here is what she found.

FOODS	STORE A	STORE B	STORE C
WHOLE WHEAT BREAD, 1½ LBS.	2 FOR $1.75	$ .99	$1.29
WHOLE MILK, ½ GAL.	.93	.90	.91
LARGE EGGS	.87	.85	.89
BACON, 1 LB.	1.29	1.36	1.25
HEAD LETTUCE, 1 HEAD	.44	.49	.45

Directions: Answer the following questions by writing the letter of the correct store in the space provided.

1. WHICH STORE HAS THE LOWEST PRICED BREAD?	
2. WHICH STORE HAS THE HIGHEST PRICE FOR MILK?	
3. WHICH STORE HAS THE LOWEST PRICE FOR EGGS?	
4. WHICH STORE HAS THE HIGHEST PRICE FOR BACON?	
5. WHERE IS LETTUCE THE CHEAPEST?	

6. What would be the total cost of buying one of each item on the list in Store A?

$_____

7. If she buys one of each item in Store B, what will she spend?

$_____

8. If she buys everything in Store C except bread, what will she spend?

$_____

9. If Pat can shop in only one store, which one should she select?

_____

Foods and Nutrition

Name   Date   Period   Score

Objective: Compute the difference in cost of food prepared at home and bought in a restaurant. **(Math)**

EATING AT A RESTAURANT OR EATING AT HOME: A COST COMPARISON

Bill and Jo-Lynn love to eat at Della's Diner, a local restaurant serving delicious homemade food. However, they feel it is expensive to eat at a restaurant regularly. They have decided to compare the costs of having a meal at Della's to eating the same food at home.

Directions: Calculate how much the following menu would cost at the diner. Bill and Jo-Lynn ordered the same foods.

Cost for One

$ .90	Vegetable soup (bowl) with crackers
3.50	Chef's salad with French dressing, roll, butter, and jelly
.80	Carrot cake
.50	Coffee (refills free at diner)

_____ Subtotal for one person

_____ Subtotal for two people

_____ 6% sales tax

_____ 15% tip (on subtotal for two people)

_____ Total cost for two people

The chart on the next page is a breakdown of the costs of buying the foods required to make the same meal that Bill and Jo-Lynn chose at Della's Diner. Please remember that there will be foods left over, beyond what they would use at one meal.

Directions: When you have completed the calculations on the next page, answer the following questions.

1. What will it cost Bill and Jo-Lynn to eat the same meal at home? $_____

2. What is the *difference* in price between eating out and eating at home? $_____

3. If Bill and Jo-Lynn had this meal, or a similar one, at a restaurant once a week for one year, what would be the total cost? $_____

4. What would it cost to serve this food at home once a week for a year? $_____

5. What is the difference in price between the two? $_____

Foods and Nutrition

EATING AT A RESTAURANT OR EATING AT HOME: A COST COMPARISON (cont.)

Directions: Please calculate the cost per serving and the price for two.
Round off each calculated amount to the nearest cent.

QUANTITY PURCHASED	ITEM	PRICE	NUMBER OF SERVINGS	COST PER SERVING	PRICE FOR TWO
1 head	Lettuce	$ .48	8	$.	$.
6 oz.	French dressing	.60	6	.	.
3½ oz. package	Turkey (sliced)	.89	4	.	.
3½ oz. package	Ham (sliced)	.99	4	.	.
6 oz. package	Sliced Swiss cheese	1.39	6	.	.
1 lb.	Tomatoes	.59	4	.	.
1 doz.	Eggs	.89	12	.	.
8	Bakery rolls	1.30	8	.	.
6 oz.	Jelly	.79	24	.	.
1 can	Vegetable soup	.30	2	.	.
1 box	Soda crackers	.69	20	.	.
1	Frozen carrot cake	2.59	6	.	.
4 oz.	Instant coffee	2.25	50 cups	.	.
1 lb.	Butter	2.39	32	.	.
			TOTAL	$.	$.

Foods and Nutrition

EATING AT A RESTAURANT OR EATING AT HOME: A COST COMPARISON (cont.)

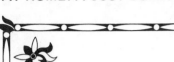

DELLA'S DINER

MENU

APPETIZERS

Served with freshly baked breads and butter.

Shrimp Cocktail	$2.35
Nachos	4.25
Guacamole	2.75

SOUPS

Soup of the Day - Always homemade, with crackers

	cup	.40
	bowl	.90

SALADS

Dressings: House, Blue Cheese Thousand Island or French

Chef's Salad Turkey, ham, cheese, tomato, hard-cooked egg	$3.50
Tuna Salad Tomato and Hard-cooked egg	3.75
Turkey Salad Tomato and Hard-cooked egg	3.75
Egg Salad Tomato	2.25
Pineapple and Cottage Cheese	2.15

All of the above salads are served with your choice of a hot roll or date-nut bread.

EGGS

Sausage and 2 eggs	$ 2.25
Ham and 2 eggs	2.25
Bacon and 2 eggs	2.25
Two eggs, any style	1.35
Ham and Cheese omelette	2.50
Denver omelette	2.50

All of the above breakfasts are served with hash brown potatoes and toast.

SIDE ORDERS

Sliced tomatoes	.60
Cole slaw	.60
Cottage cheese	.60
Potato salad	.60
English muffin	.50
Bagel	.40
Dill pickles	.30

DESSERTS

Cakes: Carrot or Chocolate	.80
ala mode	1.10
Ice Cream, 1 scoop	.60
Homemade pudding	.65
Donut	.30
Danish pastry	.75

BEVERAGES

Coffee, tea, Sanka	.50
Iced coffee, Iced tea	.50
Soft drinks	.60
Milk: Regular, 2%, nonfat, butter-milk, chocolate	.50
Hot chocolate	.50
Orange or Grapefruit juice	.40, .60
Tomato juice	.40, .60

PARENTING AND FAMILY RELATIONSHIPS
Teacher-Managed Reading Activities

BUILDING VOCABULARY

1. Name That Synonym/Antonym

This game can be used to test the student's ability to name synonyms, antonyms, or both. The objective of the game is to score the least amount of points. Divide the class into two teams. Put each word from the vocabulary list on a separate 3" x 5" card.

To begin: Player A on Side 1 chooses an index card. Player A gives the first clue to his or her side by saying a synonym/antonym for the word on the index card. If the team guesses the word after the first clue, Side 1 scores 0 points and it is then Side 2's turn. If Side 1 does not guess the word, Player A continues to give clues until they do so. Each time a clue is given and the team gives an incorrect response, the team scores 1 point.

2. Similes

Have students create similes on subjects related to parenting, e.g.:

- Being a baby is like . . .
- Disciplining a child is like . . .
- Being a teenager is like . . .

3. Metaphors

Create metaphors from words on the vocabulary list, e.g.:

- Families steer their children.
- Relationships churn the emotions.

IMPROVING COMPREHENSION

1. Classify It!

Classify similar words from the vocabulary list under one heading, e.g.:

- Body Parts
- Illnesses
- Feelings
- Expressions

(*Literal Comprehension*)

2. Without a Title

Have students read magazine articles related to parenting or family relations. Have them develop a catchy title for the excerpt. Then have them find (or draw) an illustration (hand-drawing, magazine picture, cartoon, etc.) which illustrates and enhances the article. (*Literal Comprehension*)

3. Getting the Main Idea

Have students read articles about the following topics and determine what the theme or main idea is:

- Child rearing practices
- Information pamphlets distributed by day care centers

(*Inferential Comprehension*)

4. Empathizing

Have students read articles about the following topics and ask them for ways to empathize with the people in the situation:

- A teenage girl is pregnant
- A family has just experienced the death of a family member
- The breadwinner of the family has lost his or her job

(*Inferential Comprehension*)

5. "Dear Abby"

Read "Dear Abby" columns and choose letters relating to parenting and child development. Have students determine what the most logical things to do would be. (*Applicative Comprehension*)

6. Analyzing What You Read

Have the students read articles about issues relating to child development and have them analyze the validity of the information. Divide the class into two sides with different points of view and have a class debate. (*Anaytical Comprehension*)

PARENTING AND FAMILY RELATIONSHIPS
Teacher-Managed Writing Activities

JOURNAL WRITING
(Refer to Appendix 1.)

Use the following open-ended sentences for journal entries:

- Good things that happened to me this week . . .
- The hardest thing I had to do this week . . .
- I was disappointed when . . .
- I am happy when . . .

FILMSTRIP WRITING
(Refer to Appendixes 2–4.)

Write filmstrip scripts in the narrative domain on the following topics:

- Babysitting guidelines
- How to keep children safe and healthy
- How to communicate effectively

LETTER TO THE EDITOR
(Refer to Appendix 5.)

1. Write a critical commentary about children misbehaving in stores.
2. Write about the effects of peer pressure.

CONSUMER BUSINESS LETTER
(Refer to Appendixes 6–8.)

1. Write a letter to a health insurance company about a claim which should have been paid to you. (You have paid the doctor and have waited over two months to be reimbursed.)
2. Write a letter (as if you were a parent) regarding an incorrect charge on care given to your child in a hospital, e.g., a child had tonsils out and is charged for the use of crutches!
3. Write a letter to the school counselor requesting a conference regarding a specific problem.

WRITING LISTS

(Refer to Appendix 13.)

1. List the steps to follow when playing a game with young children.
2. List the steps in taking care of an emergency medical situation for a young child, e.g.:

   - a two-year-old ate ten aspirins.
   - a three-year-old rolls off a two-foot high deck and hits his or her head on the pavement.

3. List the steps in drawing a three-generation family tree.
4. List the steps in making a family decision about an activity, e.g., where to go on a family vacation.

PARENTING AND FAMILY RELATIONSHIPS

Vocabulary List

abdomen
abnormal
abortion
abuse
adjustment
affection
afterbirth
aggressive
amniotic fluid
amniotic sac or
  bag of water
analgesic
anemia
anesthesia
announcement
antibodies
anus
areola
assertive
autism

bacteria
battered
behavior
birth
bladder
bloody show
breech

Caesarean section
ceremony
certificate
cervix
chromosomes
colostrum
conception
condom
conflicts
congenital
contagious
contraception
contraction
communication
crisis
custom

delivery
development
diaphragm
diet
dilate
dilation
dip
discipline
disease
disinfectant
divorce
douche
Down's syndrome

embryo
environment
episiotomy
expectation

fallopian tubes
family
feelings
fertility
fertilization
fetus
follicle sac
fontanel
forceps
formula
fraternal twins
frustration

gamma globulin
general anesthetic
genes
genitals
German measles
germs
gestation
gonorrhea
gynecologist

health
heredity
hormone
hymen
hysterectomy

identical twins
identity
immunity
  immunization
individuality
infant
infection
intrauterine
involution

labor
layette
lightening
local anesthetic
lochia
love

malnutrition
maternal
maternity
maturity
menopause
menstruation
mental
miscarriage
muscle

nausea
navel
newborn
normal

obstetrician
oral
osmosis
ova
ovary
ovulation
ovum

pap test (smear)
parenthood
paternal
paternity
pediatrician
pelvis
penis
physical
pituitary gland
placenta

postnatal
post partum
pregnancy
pregnant
premature
prenatal
puberty
psychomotor

quickening

rectum
relationships
responsibility
Rh factor
rhythm
role

saddle block
sedation
siblings
socialization
sperm
sterile
symptoms
syphilis

temperature
tetanus
toddler
toxic
traditional

umbilical cord
unity
urethra
urination
uterus

vaccination
vaccine
vagina
values
vernix caseosa
virus
vulva or labia

yellow body

PARENTING AND FAMILY RELATIONSHIPS

Student Worksheets—Teaching Strategies

The answers for the Parenting and Family Relationships student worksheets are found in the Answer Key, p. 227. Teaching strategies for selected student worksheets are found below.

VARIOUS FORMS OF FAMILY GOVERNMENT

This exercise is very effective in a parenting and/or relationship class at the beginning of the semester. It can lead directly into a discussion of the family life cycle. At the end of the unit or end of the semester, the students can write one or more paragraphs describing the form of family government they would prefer for themselves and the steps they need to take to insure achieving it.

Prewriting Experiences

1. Discuss how societies around the world and in various cultures in the United States organize their families.

   Examples: Traditional Oriental, Arab, Greek, Italian countries, etc. In addition, it is interesting to discuss an American Indian culture, such as the Navajos, where property is passed through the females and the females on the reservations do most of the labor.

2. *Optional:* Discussion of how students' families are organized.

Student Activities

1. Students look up dictionary definitions of various types of family governments.
2. Discuss each type and the implications for family life.

   For example: A family with small children is usually not 100% democratic because the children don't have a vote of equal value.

3. The students then write one or more paragraphs about how their own families are organized.
4. *Optional:* Role-play how each of the different types of family governments would make a decision. For example: Where to go on a family vacation. Evaluate the family structure as played in the scenes. The students can write evaluations, if desired.

PROBLEM SOLVING

Before the students begin writing their paragraphs on problem solving, there are several prewriting experiences which may be useful.

Magic Circle

"I solved a _____ X _____ problem with my parents by . . ."
"I solved a problem with an unsatisfactory garment (or car, etc.) by . . ."

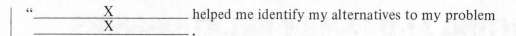

"_____X_____ helped me identify my alternatives to my problem
_____X_____ ."

Class Discussion

Discuss how to go through the steps in problem solving, using real-life examples.

After choosing a topic, the students can write their paragraphs. The editing and rewriting can be done in small groups. Only the final copies should be turned in for evaluation.

When the work is completed, the class discussion can center around individual ways the problems were solved.

HOW MUCH WILL THE WEDDING COST?

1. If you would prefer, have the students find out the costs of these types of weddings themselves. By "whiting-out" the figures in the charts before reproducing them for the students, the chart will be usable for the alternate assignment.
2. Different customs may prevail among ethnic and cultural groups. Discuss the customs and morés of your particular students and have them develop a chart of wedding costs which would be more appropriate to their heritages.

PLANNING A BUDGET AND RENTING AN APARTMENT

Discuss why people spend what they do, the reasons for looking at a budget as a pie to be divided, the consequences of spending more than earned, etc. Explain to students that the circle graph and information on budgets needs to be used for the Renting an Apartment exercise.

Parenting and Family Relationships

Name _____   Date _____   Period _____   Score _____

Objective: Identify details using written material. **(Reading)**

INVITATION

> *Mr. and Mrs. John Jackson*
> *and*
> *Mr. and Mrs. Fred Ferguson*
> *invite you to share in the joy*
> *of the marriage uniting*
> *Laura Jean Jackson*
> *and*
> *James G. Ferguson*
> *Saturday the tenth of March*
> *at eleven o'clock*
> *Carson City Community Church*
> *Carson City, Nevada*
> *Luncheon reception immediately following*

> _____ *person(s)*
> *will attend*
> *from the*
> _____
> *Household*
> *R.S.V.P. by March 3*

Directions: Please circle the letter of the best answer.

1. This invitation is to what kind of event?
   a. shower
   b. birthday
   c. wedding
   d. retirement

2. The reception will be held on
   a. March 11
   b. March 10
   c. March 15
   d. March 3

3. The parents are (2 best answers)
   a. Mr. and Mrs. James Ferguson
   b. Mr. and Mrs. John Jackson
   c. Mr. and Mrs. L. Jean Jackson
   d. Mr. and Mrs. Fred Ferguson

4. The event itself begins at
   a. 11:00 a.m.
   b. 11:00 p.m.
   c. 3:00 p.m.
   d. 10:00 a.m.

5. The guest(s) attending must indicate which of the following by March 3? (2 best answers)
   a. What they will be wearing
   b. How many persons will be attending
   c. The name of the family attending
   d. Where the family lives

Parenting and Family Relationships

Name   Date   Period   Score

Objectives: Interpret charts and graphs; do simple computations. **(Reading; Math)**

UNDERSTANDING TEMPERATURE READINGS

Six-year-old John has the flu. His temperature has been up and down over a two-day period. His mother has kept a record of his temperature to give to the doctor.

   Directions: Study the chart below and circle the letter of the best answers to each question.

John's Temperature Chart			
Monday		**Tuesday**	
6:00 a.m.	101 degrees	6:00 a.m.	101 degrees
12 noon	99 degrees	12 noon	100 degrees
6:00 p.m.	103 degrees	6:00 p.m.	99.5 degrees

1. What is the difference between John's highest and lowest recorded temperature?

   a. 4.00 degrees

   b. 3.40 degrees

   c. 3.00 degrees

2. What was the difference between 6 a.m. and noon on Tuesday?

   a. 1 degree

   b. 2 degrees

   c. ½ degree

3. The average temperature for John on Monday was

   a. 99.3 degrees

   b. 101.0 degrees

   c. 101.3 degrees

4. The difference between the highest temperature and a normal temperature (98.6) was

   a. 4.4 degrees

   b. 5 degrees

   c. 4.0 degrees

Parenting and Family Relationships

Name _____ Date _____ Period _____ Score _____

Objective: Use the dictionary for entry word information. **(Reading)**

VARIOUS FORMS OF FAMILY GOVERNMENT

Directions: Families, like governments, are organized in various ways.
Using a dictionary, define the following terms.

Patriarchal _____

_____

Matriarchal _____

_____

Democratic _____

_____

Anarchistic _____

_____

Autocratic _____

_____

In a dictionary, look up the word defining a *type* of family.

Nuclear family _____

_____

Extended family _____

_____

Blended family _____

_____

Single-parent family _____

_____

_____

Parenting and Family Relationships

Name _____   Date _____ Period _____ Score _____

Objective: Write paragraphs of description. **(Writing)**

YOUR FAMILY GOVERNMENT

Directions: How is your own family organized? Check the category you
feel most closely applies:

Patriarchal _____   Matriarchal _____   Democratic _____

Autocratic _____   Anarchistic _____

Check the category which most closely describes your type of family:

Nuclear _____   Extended _____   Blended _____   Single-parent _____

In the space below, write one or more paragraphs which describe how
your own family unit is organized. Include such information as who
makes the decisions, who helps whom, etc. *Optional:* How do you
feel about this type of structure?

_____

_____

_____

_____

_____

_____

_____

_____

_____

_____

_____

_____

_____

_____

Parenting and Family Relationships

Name _____ Date _____ Period _____ Score _____

Objective: Write a friendly letter. **(Writing)**

PERSONAL (FRIENDLY) LETTERS

Directions: Do one of the following:

1. Write a thank-you letter to someone who has given you something or done something nice for you. For example: Your best friend gave you a nice belt for your birthday. Include information about how well it goes with certain clothes, as well as your pleasure at his or her thoughtfulness.
2. Write a thank-you letter to a person who has written a job recommendation for you. This letter should be slightly more formal than a gift thank-you note. Be sure to include your appreciation for the *time and effort* they extended in writing for you! This is a smart and professional action which will help you in your job searches in the future.

_____

_____

_____

_____ ,

_____

_____

_____

_____

_____

_____

_____

_____

_____

_____

_____

_____

_____

Parenting and Family Relationships

Name _____ Date _____ Period _____ Score _____

Objective: Address an envelope for a friendly letter. (Writing)

ENVELOPE FOR FRIENDLY LETTER

Directions: Fill in both envelopes.

Staggered Address

Flush-Left Address, Centered ZIP Code

Parenting and Family Relationships

Name _____ Date _____ Period _____ Score _____

Objective: Write paragraphs revealing cause and effect. **(Writing)**

PROBLEM SOLVING

Problem solving is a rather complex process. However, if the following steps are taken, it is possible to arrive at a good solution to a problem.

Steps in Problem Solving

1. Identify the problem
2. Determine the alternatives
3. Evaluate each alternative
4. Choose what seems to be the best alternative
5. Accept the consequences (list them)

Directions: Select one of the following problems. Write a paragraph describing the steps needed to solve the problem. Use correct paragraph form, complete sentences, and correct spelling and punctuation.

Problems—Level I

1. You lost a contact lens in the hall during lunch.
2. You spilled water on your term paper due next period.
3. You missed your only ride to school.
4. You lost the heel from your shoe.
5. Your wallet was stolen at school.
6. You made a date with two people for the same night.
7. You got paint on your best shirt in art class.

_____

_____

_____

_____

_____

_____

_____

_____

_____

_____

_____

_____

Parenting and Family Relationships

PROBLEM SOLVING (cont.)

Problems—Level II

Now that you know how to solve a simple problem, try your hand at solving a more difficult problem. Write a paragraph describing how you would solve one of the following problems. Follow the "Steps in Problem Solving." Use correct paragraph form, complete sentences, and correct spelling and punctuation.

1. You need a part-time job and are under 18.
2. You need a means of financing senior year expenses.
3. You have many personal expenses including the need for new clothing.
4. You need to buy a car or motorcycle.
5. You need to plan how to finance your college education.
6. You need to plan job training after high school.
7. You want to finance a vacation with friends.

Parenting and Family Relationships

Name   Date   Period   Score

Objective: Write descriptions of personal feelings and moods, using sensory words. **(Writing)**

IT HAPPENED THIS WAY . . .

Directions: After discussing positive and negative things that happened to you this week, write what you mentioned (or thought about) in a paragraph. Use complete sentences as well as correct spelling and punctuation.

"A positive/good thing that happened to me this week was. . . .
It was good for me because. . . ."

_____

_____

_____

_____

_____

_____

_____

"A negative/bad thing that happened to me this week was. . . . It was
bad for me because. . . ."

_____

_____

_____

_____

_____

_____

_____

Parenting and Family Relationships

Name _____   Date _____ Period _____ Score _____

Objective: Write an essay to defend one's own values. **(Writing)**

TAKING A POSITION

Many situations in life are complicated, and making a decision or taking a position is often difficult. The best decisions are based on a person's values and goals in life.

Directions: To gain practice in developing rational positions on controversial subjects, participate in class activities and write out your feelings about a given topic. You may write your paper in any one of several ways: a poem, a position paper, a persuasive paper trying to get another to join in your position, or an editorial for the school newspaper. Use complete sentences as well as correct spelling and punctuation. Write on a separate page.

Choose One of the Following Topics:

Child abuse	Drug abuse
Single parent	Working mother
Divorce	Open adoption records

My Topic: _____

I will be writing (check one):

_____ a poem   _____ a position paper

_____ a persuasive paper   _____ an editorial

One or more values that I hold which influences my position (please list):

_____

_____

_____

One or more of my goals which will be affected by my position:

_____

_____

_____

_____

_____

_____

DATE DUE _____

Parenting and Family Relationships

Name _____ Date _____ Period _____ Score _____

Objective: Write paragraphs of simple exposition. **(Writing)**

FEELINGS

For various reasons, our feelings are often kept hidden. Perhaps we are afraid to show them because others may not know how to react or because we wish to keep them to ourselves. But it is good to express feelings, at least some of them, because that is what makes us human.

Directions: Please write out the personal feelings you might have if you were faced with the following situations:

1. You have not completed the report you knew was due, and your teacher just asked for it.

_____

_____

_____

_____

2. You overhear two "friends" talking about you in an uncomplimentary way.

_____

_____

_____

_____

3. Your friends all want to go somewhere you have been forbidden to go.

_____

_____

_____

_____

4. A friend asks you to give him or her the answer to a test question and/or your friend asks to copy your homework.

_____

_____

_____

Parenting and Family Relationships

Name _____ Date _____ Period _____ Score _____

Objective: Compose paragraphs with complete sentences and correct punctuation and spelling. **(Writing)**

GOOD PARENTS...

Directions: Write two paragraphs in the spaces below. Use a topic sentence, correct spelling and punctuation, and complete sentences.

Topic 1: "The parent I would like to be...

_____

_____

_____

_____

_____

_____

_____

_____

_____

* * *

Topic 2: "A person who greatly influenced my life...

_____

_____

_____

_____

_____

_____

_____

_____

_____

Parenting and Family Relationships

Name _____ Date _____ Period _____ Score _____

Objective: Write paragraphs that develop opinions or values supported by specific facts. **(Writing)**

PARENTING/CHILD DEVELOPMENT TOPICS

Directions: Choose one of the topics listed below. Write one paragraph describing the advantages of each alternative and a second paragraph describing the disadvantages. In the third paragraph, describe what your own personal decision would be in the situation, based on the advantages and disadvantages you described in the first and second paragraphs. Use complete sentences and correct spelling and punctuation.

Topics

- Bottle feeding vs. breast feeding
- Strict discipline vs. permissive discipline
- Rooming-in hospital maternity care vs. nursery hospital maternity care
- Hospital delivery vs. home delivery
- Group day care vs. individual day care
- Mothers of young children working outside the home vs. mothers staying at home

Topic: _____

1. Advantages: _____

_____

_____

_____

_____

2. Disadvantages: _____

_____

_____

_____

_____

3. My Personal Decision: _____

_____

_____

_____

_____

Parenting and Family Relationships

Name _____ Date _____ Period _____ Score _____

Objective: Write a short library paper based on several different sources. **(Writing)**

RESEARCH PAPERS

Here are some ways to organize your ideas and begin writing.

1. There are many sources of information. Your teacher may have pamphlets from the government printing office. If not, he or she can tell you how to order them. In addition, you can use books and other materials from your classroom and from your school and public library.

2. Practice summarizing information from your sources. Remember, if you write the information in your own words, you do not have to put quotation marks around it. You do need quotation marks, however, if you quote your source.

3. Use at least three sources for your paper. Practice writing footnotes and bibliography entries. Whenever you write information from one of your sources, you must have a footnote reference to that source, whether the information is a direct quotation or is written in your own words.

4. After you have gathered your information, you will need to organize it. You will need to write introductions, topic sentences, supporting statements, conclusions, etc.

5. Edit your paper. You may do this with a partner or in a small group.

6. Neatly write or type your final draft, with footnotes and a bibliography. Put your report in a report cover, either purchased or handmade.

Suggestions for Research Paper Topics

1. Teenage Marriages
2. Teenage Mothers (and/or Pregnancies)
3. Single Parents
4. Children's Responsibilities in a Single-Parent Family
5. Child Abuse
6. Alcohol in Family Conflicts
7. Teenage Venereal Disease
8. Families Headed by Women
9. The Special Problems and Joys in Extended Families
10. Financial Problems in Families Headed by Women
11. The Special Problems of Children with Working Mothers
12. Changing Family Roles
13. Changing Family Relationships
14. Generation Gap Conflicts in Families
15. The Trials and Tribulations of Blended Families
16. Death and Divorce—Their Effect on Family Life

Parenting and Family Relationships

Name   Date   Period   Score

Objectives: Write paragraphs that develop opinions or values supported by specific facts; change two different units of measurement to one unit and compute the sum of several amounts of money. **(Writing; Math)**

HAPPY BIRTHDAY

You are planning a birthday celebration for your child's seventh birthday. He has two friends you plan to bring along. To help you decide which place you might attend, you have decided to compare costs at each. Because you plan to bring a picnic lunch, you will only need to buy 2 cold drinks per person.

Who will be attending: 1 adult (5'8"), 1 adult (5'11")
3 children, about 7 years old (4'1", 3'11" and 4'2")

Directions: Calculate the total cost for 5 people to go to each place. Put your answer in the "Total Cost" column.

PER PERSON COST

PLACE	ADULTS	CHILDREN	TWO COLD DRINKS	5 PEOPLE TOTAL COST
THE ZOO	$ 3.00	$1.00	$1.00	$.
HAPPY MOUNTAIN PARK	48" & over $10.95	48" & under $5.95	$2.00	$.
FANTASY PARK	$ 9.25	$7.50	$1.80	$.
STAR STUDIO TOUR	$ 8.95	$6.95	$1.70	$.

In the space below, indicate where *you* would go, and the reasons for your choice.

_____

_____

_____

_____

_____

_____

Extra Credit: Find out how much it would cost for the same people to eat at a pizza parlor, or to have ice cream desserts and beverages at an ice cream parlor.

Parenting and Family Relationships

Name _____ Date _____ Period _____ Score _____

Objective: Add numbers, regrouping as necessary. **(Math)**

ROCK CONCERT TICKETS

Todd and Brent are planning to attend a rock concert to be held at the Amphitheater. Because the concert is still several months away, they will have their choice of seats.

DAYS	TIME	PRICE		
		SECTION A	SECTION B	SECTIONS C&D
TUESDAY–THURSDAY	8:00	$17.00	$14.00	$ 8.00
FRIDAY	8:00	18.50	15.50	9.50
SATURDAY	8:00	20.50	17.50	11.50
SATURDAY & SUNDAY MATINEES	2:30	13.00	10.00	6.50

Directions: Calculate the cost of 2 tickets for prices and dates below:

Total for Two

1. Tuesday, section B $_____

2. Friday, section C $_____

3. Saturday, section A $_____

4. Sunday, section B $_____

5. What is the difference in cost $_____
   of 2 tickets in sections A and C
   on Tuesday evening?

6. What is the difference in cost $_____
   of 2 tickets in sections A and B
   at the Saturday matinee?

7. If Todd and Brent decide on $_____
   Friday in section B, how much
   change will they receive from a
   $50.00 bill?

8. If you were going to this concert, what section would you choose?

   Section _____. Why?

Parenting and Family Relationships

Name _____   Date _____   Period _____   Score _____

Objective: Use mathematics to organize an approach to problem solving. **(Math)**

HOW MUCH WILL THE WEDDING COST?

Directions: The chart below shows examples of prices for various types of weddings. Please study the chart and answer the questions below. There will be 100 guests at the wedding.

ITEMS	COUNTRY CLUB OR HOTEL	CHURCH AND RECEPTION	CHURCH AND SWEET TABLE	HOME AND RECEPTION
Minister or justice of the peace	$ 75.00	$ 75.00	$ 75.00	$ 75.00
Building rental	500.00	100.00	100.00	XX
Flowers	300.00	250.00	150.00	150.00
Food	sit-down dinner 1,500.00	supper buffet 400.00	150.00	150.00
Liquor	750.00	XX	XX	200.00
Clothing—2 adults, bride, sister of the bride	500.00	500.00	500.00	300.00
Music	500.00	75.00	75.00	30.00
Gifts for 4 attendants	80.00	80.00	80.00	80.00
Pictures (professional photography)	650.00	650.00	650.00	100.00*
TOTALS	$	$	$	$

*Note: A friend will take photographs. You will pay for film and processing.

1. What are the totals of each type of wedding? (List in spaces provided above.)

2. If you have $1,000 to spend on the wedding, what will be the type of wedding you could choose?

   _____

3. If you have $3,000, what type can you choose? _____

4. If you decided not to serve liquor at your home wedding, you can lower the cost by

   a. $675.00   c. $200.00

   b. $750.00   d. $0

Parenting and Family Relationships

HOW MUCH WILL THE WEDDING COST? (cont.)

5. The food cost for a country club or hotel wedding is about
   $15.00 per person. How much per person is the food at the
   church reception?

   a. $1.50   c. $2.50

   b. $15.00   d. $4.00

6. List 5 ways to reduce the cost of these or any weddings.
   (Do not suggest eloping!)

   a. _____

   b. _____

   c. _____

   d. _____

   e. _____

Parenting and Family Relationships

Name _____ Date _____ Period _____ Score _____

Objectives: Calculate monthly expenses; write a paragraph of simple exposition. **(Math, Writing)**

PLANNING A BUDGET

Jane and Bruce are planning to be married. They are starting to decide how they can make their $1,900 a month take-home pay cover all the expenses of moving into an apartment, setting up housekeeping, and paying all of their regular monthly expenses.

After much discussion, Jane and Bruce decide they need to spend a certain percentage of their income on rent, a certain percentage on food, on transportation, etc. The circle graph below represents their decisions about how they will divide up their combined take-home income.

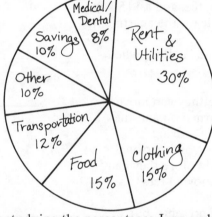

Directions: After studying the percentages Jane and Bruce decided upon, calculate in *dollars* their monthly living expenses. Write your calculations in the spaces provided. The total should equal the monthly take-home pay.

Rent and Utilities	$_____
Food	$_____
Transportation (1 car)	$_____
Medical/Dental	$_____
Clothing	$_____
Savings	$_____
Other	$_____
Grand Total	$_____

If you were in their situation, would you spend your income differently? _____

In what way would you make changes?

_____

_____

Parenting and Family Relationships

Name   Date   Period   Score

Objectives: Make calculations involved in renting an apartment; write short paragraphs revealing cause and effect. **(Math, Writing)**

RENTING AN APARTMENT

Jane and Bruce plan to be married shortly and are looking for an apartment. The one they found which suits them best has one bedroom. It is quite close to their work locations. The rent is $450 per month; only the water is paid for by the landlord. They figure that utilities will cost approximately $120 per month.

   Jane and Bruce want to sign a lease, but to do so, they must make certain types of payments. They need to pay the first and last month's rent, a $75 security deposit (refundable when they vacate the apartment, if they leave it in good condition), a $100 cleaning fee, and a $15 key deposit. The key deposit is refundable when they leave the apartment.

1. What is the total Jane and Bruce must pay to the landlord when they sign their lease? $_____

2. Jane and Bruce will have other expenses before they can move in. It will cost them $80 to have the utilities turned on and the telephone connected. In addition, they will have moving expenses of $350 to have their furniture, clothes, and personal effects moved. What is the total they will spend before they can move in, including rent, deposits, utilities, and moving fees? $_____

3. Jane and Bruce will be receiving some wedding presents, but they will still need to buy some basics such as cleaning supplies and equipment, a vacuum cleaner, dish towels, etc. They figure these items will cost at least $250. What is the grand total of expenses facing them before they can move into their new apartment and set up housekeeping? $_____

4. While looking for an apartment, they found a two-bedroom, two-bath apartment which they liked very much. The rent was $595 per month, which was only $145 more per month than the one-bedroom they selected. Why did Jane and Bruce think they could not afford this apartment on their $1,900 a month take-home pay?

   _____

   _____

5. If they *really* wanted to live in this larger apartment, what adjustments in their budget would you suggest which would provide them with the extra $145 a month they need?

   _____

6. Would you be willing to make those same sacrifices to have the larger apartment? _____ Why or why not? _____

Parenting and Family Relationships

Name _____   Date _____ Period _____ Score _____

Objective: Compute the lowest cost per unit. **(Math)**

RESEARCHING THE COST OF BABY FOODS

Directions: In the local supermarket, find the prices of the six baby foods in the chart. Complete the chart and calculate the cost per ounce of each food.

Prices for Commercially Prepared Baby Foods

ITEM	BRAND	JAR SIZE	PRICE	COST PER OUNCE
Pureed peas		oz.	$	$
Pureed green beans		oz.	$	$
Chopped beef		oz.	$	$
Oat cereal (instant)		oz.	$	$
Vanilla pudding		oz.	$	$
Beef-vegetable comb.		oz.	$	$

Directions: Find the prices of the nine foods in the chart. Complete the chart and calculate the cost per ounce of each food.

Prices for Foods which can be Prepared at Home

ITEM	SIZE OF PACKAGE AS PURCHASED	PRICE	COST PER OUNCE
Frozen peas	oz.	$	$
Frozen green beans	oz.	$	$
Round steak	oz.	$	$
Oatmeal (instant)	oz.	$	$
Instant vanilla pudding	oz.	$	$
Milk for pudding	oz.	$	$
Chuck roast	oz.	$	$
Carrots	oz.	$	$
Potatoes	oz.	$	$

Parenting and Family Relationships

Name _____   Date _____   Period _____   Score _____

Objective: Use mathematics to organize an approach to problem solving. **(Math)**

LANDMARKS IN BABY'S GROWTH

Story

You are a new parent and are very excited about the birth of your infant. You really care about his or her growth and development and are anxious to know when he or she will go through various stages of emotional, physical, and social growth. The graph shows the approximate ages at which these stages of growth take place.

Directions: Calculate the dates (including year) on which your baby will arrive at the various landmarks in growth. Determine a birthdate before you begin your calculations.

BIRTHDATE _____ , 19 _____

Dates of landmarks in growth for your baby.

_____ Sense of trust   _____ Often negative, responds with "NO"

_____ Smiles at caregiver   _____ Engages in solitary play

_____ Cries when put down   _____ Is interested in other children

_____ Shows anger   _____ Engages in parallel play

_____ Shows fear   _____ May show jealousy

_____ Cries when strangers approach   _____ Responds to spoken commands

_____ Unpredictable emotions   _____ Engages in cooperative play

_____ Can distract   _____ Engages in group play

Parenting and Family Relationships

LANDMARKS IN BABY'S GROWTH (cont.)

4 YEARS _____

Engages in group play

Engages in cooperative play

3 YEARS _____

Responds to spoken commands

May show jealousy

Engages in parallel play

2 YEARS _____

Is interested in other children

Engages in solitary play

Often negative, responds with "NO"
Can distract

Unpredictable emotions

1 YEAR _____

Cries when strangers approach
Shows fear

Shows anger

Cries when put down
Smiles at caregiver
Sense of trust

BIRTH _____

Parenting and Family Relationships

Name   Date   Period   Score

Objective: Use mathematics to organize an approach to problem-solving. **(Math)**

SELECTING INFANT CLOTHING

Directions: Mary and John are purchasing clothing for their newborn infant. They found a sale at a store selling baby clothes. Study the advertisement and use the information to answer the questions below.

BEA'S BABY BOUTIQUE
* * *

	Regular Price	Sale Price
Infant gowns	$2.00	$1.50
Infant shirts	1.00	.89
Diapers	5.95/dozen	4.50/dozen

1. How much can they save if they buy 2 gowns at the sale price?

   a. $2.50

   b. $1.50

   c. $1.00

2. What is the difference in price between 1 shirt at regular price and at sale price?

   a. $ .11

   b. $ .12

   c. $ .01

3. They need 4 dozen diapers and have only $15. How many dozen diapers can they buy on sale?

   a. 1 dozen

   b. 3 dozen

   c. 2 dozen

4. If they buy 2 gowns, 4 infant shirts, and 4 dozen diapers on sale, how much will they spend?

   a. $34.56

   b. $25.46

   c. $24.56

5. What is the 6% sales tax on the correct total from #4 above?

   a. $1.47

   b. $1.53

   c. $1.99

6. If there were no more infant shirts on the sale table, what would be the total cost of 4 gowns and 3 dozen diapers on sale, and 3 infant shirts at regular price?

   a. $24.86

   b. $22.50

   c. $35.56

Parenting and Family Relationships

Name _____ Date _____ Period _____ Score _____

Objective: Compute the elapsed time in a given situation. **(Math)**

AGES AT WHICH SHOTS SHOULD BE GIVEN

IMMUNIZATION NEEDED	MONTHS					YEARS	
	2	4	6	15	18	4–6	14–16
Diphtheria/Pertussis/Tetanus	X	X	X		X	X	
Polio	X	X			X	X	
Measles				X			
Rubella				X			
Mumps				X			
Diphtheria/Tetanus							X

Directions: Your baby was born May 5, 1985. Please list the dates, including year, when your child will need to have immunizations.

DATES, INCLUDING YEAR

Diphtheria/Pertussis/Tetanus	_____ , _____ , _____ , _____ , _____
Polio	_____ , _____ , _____ , _____
Measles	_____
Rubella	_____
Mumps	_____
Diphtheria/Tetanus	_____

CLOTHING AND TEXTILES

Teacher-Managed Reading Activities

BUILDING VOCABULARY

1. Word Identification

Using the clothing and textile vocabulary list in this section, have students identify *specific* words that fall into the following categories:

- specific parts of a sewing machine
- specific types of fabrics
- specific notions used in sewing
- specific sewing terminology

2. Alliteration

Using the Clothing and Textiles Vocabulary List, have students make up alliterations from words on the list. An alliteration is the repetition of a sound or consonant in two or more neighboring words or syllables, e.g., wild and woolly.

3. Applying Vocabulary Knowledge

Have students utilize new words from the Clothing and Textiles Vocabulary List in a story, poem, or article title, e.g.:

- What Clothing Says about Me
- The Latest Clothing Fad
- The Last Time I Did the Family Wash

IMPROVING COMPREHENSION

1. Main Ideas

Have students read magazine articles related to clothing and have them identify the main ideas:

- in paragraphs
- by selecting the best title
- by matching a picture with a paragraph that describes it
- by selecting the statement that best expresses the main idea

2. Pattern Instructions

Distribute directions from a sewing pattern, and have the students cut the directions into the different steps. Put the steps into an envelope, preparing one envelope for each student. Have students arrange the steps into the proper sequence. This activity can also be done in teams. (*Literal Comprehension*)

3. Fabrics

Bring various fabrics to class and have students read their descriptions and characteristics in a textbook. Let the students feel the textures of the different fabrics and have them compare and contrast the differences in texture. (*Inferential Comprehension*)

4. Accessories

Bring to class scarves, jewelry, belts, and articles related to accessorizing. Have the students determine the most interesting and unique thing to do with each of the given accessories. (*Applicative Comprehension*)

CLOTHING AND TEXTILES

Teacher-Managed Writing Activities

JOURNAL WRITING
(Refer to Appendix 1.)

Use the following open-ended sentences to give students the opportunity to practice their writing skills:

- My clothes . . .
- I look . . .
- Sewing makes me . . .
- I could improve my personal appearance . . .
- In a clothing store I . . .
- Clothing means a lot . . .

FILMSTRIP WRITING
(Refer to Appendixes 2–4.)

Write dialogue for a filmstrip script utilizing two voices. Choose one of these topics:

- Current fashion trends on campus
- Sewing tips for the beginner
- Helpful hints for the care of clothing

LETTER TO THE EDITOR
(Refer to Appendix 5.)

Write an editorial aimed toward a wide audience. Choose one of these topics:

- Status symbol clothes
- Wearing jeans that are too tight
- New fabrics that are on the market

CONSUMER BUSINESS LETTER
(Refer to Appendix 6.)

1. Write a letter to a fabric store manager requesting that the pattern store save discarded pattern books for your class.
2. Write a letter of complaint about X yards of X type of fabric which shrunk X inches. Include place and date of purchase.

WRITING LISTS
(Refer to Appendix 13.)

1. List the steps in completing a simple construction task.
2. List the steps in planning a vacation wardrobe to X place.

CLOTHING AND TEXTILES

Vocabulary List

accent
accessory
acetate
acrylic
adjacent
allowance
alteration
antiperspirant
apparel
appearance

basic
baste
bids
blend
blindstitch
bobbin
bodice
body
braid
bulky
bust
button

canvas
clothing
cocoon
color
colorfast
complementary
contrast
coordinate
corduroy
cotton
crewel
crosswise
curve
cut

dart
decorate
design
detergent
diagonal
diagram
distilled water
drape
durability
durable
dye

ease
edging
embroidery

fabric
fashion
fastener
fiber
filament
filling yarn
findings
finish
firm weave
flame resistant
flax
fringe

gathers
gauge
glossy
gore
grain line
groom
gusset

harmonize
hem
horizontal

inventory

knit
knot

label
laminate
lapel
lapped
laundry
layering
layout
lengthwise
linen
lingerie
lint
loop

machine
man-made
measurement

mercerized
mesh
mildew
monochromatic

nip
neckline
needlepoint
needles
neutral
notion
nylon

occasion
odor
off grain
orlon
oval

pattern
personality
perspiration
pile
pins
plaid
pleat
polyester
press
primary
print

quality
quilt

ravel
rayon
reinforce
reversible

sanforized
scissor
Scotchguard
seam
seasonal
secondary color
selvage
sewing machine
shade
shape
shears

sheer
stain
silk
size
sizing
spool
square
stripe
style
symbol

tag
tailor tack
tape
texture
thimble
thread
tint
trim
tweed

understitch
unit

velveteen
vertical
vest

waistband
wardrobe
warp yarn
water repellent
weave
wool
woven
wrinkle

yardage
yarn

zigzag
zipper

CLOTHING AND TEXTILES

Student Worksheets—Teaching Strategies

The answers for the Clothing and Textiles student worksheets are found in the Answer Key, p. 227. Teaching strategies for a selected student worksheet are found below.

PARTS OF THE SEWING MACHINE

The student materials are copies of drawings of three major types of machines. If your machine(s) are a different brand or significantly different in model number and appearance, and if a copy of the instruction manual is available, photocopy the drawings, alphabetize the parts, and create a page similar to the student materials in this guide.

Clothing and Textiles

Name   Date   Period   Score

Objective: Interpret symbols. **(Reading)**

PATTERN SYMBOLS

Directions: Circle the letter of the words which best complete each statement.

SYMBOL	MEANING & NOTATIONS
	1. This symbol means a. stitching line. b. straight of grain. c. cutting line.
	2. This symbol means a. fold, do not cut here. b. fold, cut here. c. place on selvage.
	3. This symbol means a. cutting line. b. cutting line and seam line. c. cutting line and notch.
5/8	4. This measurement means a. size of hem line. b. depth of cutting line. c. size of seam line.

Clothing and Textiles

Name   Date   Period   Score

Objective: Classify information. **(Reading)**

UNDERSTANDING CLASSIFICATIONS

Directions: Each horizontal line of words contains one term that does not belong with the other three. Circle the one that does not belong.

1.	presser foot	tension unit	spool	thread guide
2.	pins	shears	hooks and eyes	pleats
3.	tailor's chalk	iron	sleeve board	seam roll
4.	hook and eye	needle	button	zipper
5.	baste stitch	whip stitch	blind stitch	tailor tack
6.	darts	notches	grainline	back stitch
7.	silk	polyester	wool	cotton
8.	tracing wheel	hemmer	dressmaker's carbon	tailor's chalk
9.	polyester	nylon	acrylic	linen
10.	fusible web	lengthwise grain	bias	crosswise grain

Clothing and Textiles

Name _____ Date _____ Period _____ Score _____

Objective: Interpret drawings and charts. **(Reading)**

UNDERSTANDING THIS PATTERN ENVELOPE

Directions: Study the pattern envelope, shown here and on the next page, and answer the following questions.

1. How many yards of 45″ fabric is needed to make robe A, size large? _____ yds.

2. How many yards of 60″ fabric is required to make a lining, size medium, for robe A or C? _____ yds.

3. What type of fabric is not suited for this pattern? _____

4. Are the sleeves full length? Yes _____ No _____

5. Where are the pockets? _____

6. What does * mean? _____

7. List two recommended fabrics. _____ and _____

8. What is the United States address of the pattern company?

_____

_____

_____

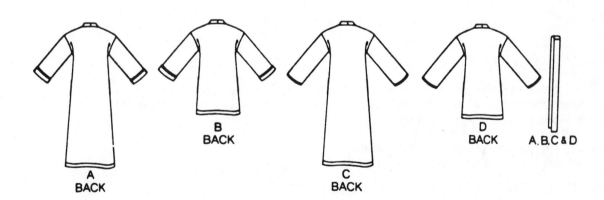

A
BACK

B
BACK

C
BACK

D
BACK

A, B, C & D

SUPERIOR PATTERNS, 175 West 79th Street, NEW YORK, NEW YORK 10024
LONDON • TORONTO • SYDNEY   PRINTED IN U.S.A.

3724 UNISEX ROBE AND BELT   6 PIECES

Loose-fitting robe in two lengths has optional lining, wrap front,
front neck bands, dropped shoulders, three-quarter length sleeves
with optional contrast lining which can be worn rolled up, side
seam pockets and topstitching. Self-tie belt. Purchased pants.
NOTE: (1) Front and back body will have optional lining and
inside sleeves will be lined at all times. (2) Robes will be shorter
on male.

BODY MEASUREMENTS

Chest or Bust	30–32	34–36	38–40	42–44	46–48
Waist	24–26	28–30	32–34	36–39	42–44
Hip (Seat)	31–33	35–37	39–41	43–45	47–49
CHEST OR BUST	30–32	34–36	38–40	42–44	46–48
SIZE	X-Small	Small	Medium	Large	X-Large

ROBE AND BELT A

44/45"*/**	$4\frac{1}{8}$	$4\frac{1}{2}$	$4\frac{3}{4}$	$5\frac{1}{8}$	$5\frac{7}{8}$
60"*/**	$3\frac{1}{4}$	$3\frac{3}{8}$	$3\frac{1}{2}$	$3\frac{3}{4}$	$4\frac{1}{4}$

ROBE AND BELT B

35"*/**	$3\frac{3}{4}$	$3\frac{7}{8}$	$4\frac{3}{8}$	$4\frac{1}{2}$	$4\frac{7}{8}$
44/45"*/**	$3\frac{1}{4}$	$3\frac{1}{4}$	$3\frac{3}{8}$	$3\frac{1}{2}$	$3\frac{3}{4}$
60"*/**	$2\frac{1}{4}$	$2\frac{1}{4}$	$2\frac{3}{8}$	$2\frac{7}{8}$	3

CONTRAST SLEEVE LINING A OR B

35,44/45"*/**	$1\frac{1}{4}$	$1\frac{1}{4}$	$1\frac{1}{4}$	$1\frac{1}{4}$	$1\frac{1}{4}$
60"*/**	$\frac{5}{8}$	$\frac{3}{4}$	$\frac{3}{4}$	$\frac{3}{4}$	$\frac{3}{4}$

ROBE AND BELT C

44/45"*/**	$4\frac{5}{8}$	$5\frac{3}{4}$	6	$6\frac{1}{4}$	$7\frac{1}{8}$
60"*/**	$3\frac{1}{2}$	4	4	$4\frac{3}{8}$	$4\frac{3}{4}$

ROBE LINING A or C (optional)

44/45"	$3\frac{3}{8}$	$3\frac{3}{8}$	$3\frac{1}{2}$	$3\frac{1}{2}$	$3\frac{7}{8}$

ROBE AND BELT D

35"*/**	$4\frac{5}{8}$	$4\frac{3}{4}$	$5\frac{5}{8}$	$5\frac{3}{4}$	6
44/45"*/**	$3\frac{3}{4}$	$3\frac{3}{4}$	$4\frac{1}{2}$	$4\frac{5}{8}$	$4\frac{3}{4}$
60"*/**	$2\frac{7}{8}$	$2\frac{7}{8}$	$2\frac{7}{8}$	$3\frac{1}{2}$	$3\frac{1}{2}$

ROBE LINING B OR D (optional)

44/45"	$2\frac{1}{8}$	$2\frac{1}{8}$	$2\frac{1}{4}$	$2\frac{1}{4}$	$2\frac{3}{8}$

Obvious diagonals – unsuitable. One-way designs – use nap fabric and layouts. Allow
extra fabric to match plaids and stripes.

*with nap, shading, pile or one-way design.
**without nap, shading or pile or with a two-way design.

WIDTH AT LOWER EDGE (excluding overlap)

Robe A, C	$58\frac{1}{2}$	$62\frac{3}{4}$	67	$72\frac{1}{4}$	$75\frac{1}{2}$
Robe B, D	$47\frac{1}{2}$	$51\frac{3}{4}$	56	$60\frac{1}{4}$	$64\frac{1}{2}$
Finished back length from base of neck					
Robe A, C	55	$56\frac{1}{2}$	58	$59\frac{1}{2}$	61
Robe B, D	$32\frac{1}{2}$	34	$35\frac{1}{2}$	37	$38\frac{1}{2}$

FABRICS: Soft or crisp fabrics: Broadcloth, Challis, Crepe Back Satin, Silk Broadcloth,
Tissue Faille and Flannelette for Robe, Belt and Sleeve Lining.

Clothing and Textiles

Name _____   Date _____ Period _____ Score _____

Objective: Match appropriate answers. **(Reading)**

PARTS OF THE BERNINA SEWING MACHINE

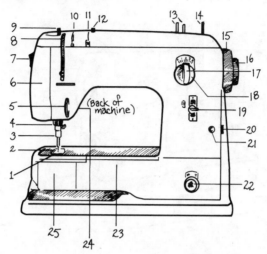

Bobbin case cover
Bobbin winder spindle
Bobbin winder tension
Control knob for drop feed
Feed dog
Free arm
Handwheel (flywheel)
Handwheel (flywheel) release
Light cover
Light switch
Needle clamp
Needle (throat) plate
Needle position control knob

Presser foot lever
Satin stitch and buttonhole regulator
Satin stitch stop lever
Sewing foot
Spool pins
Stitch length regulator/reverse lever
Stitch width knob
Tension centering wheel
Tension indicator window
Thread guide
Thread take-up lever
Thread tension discs and slot

Directions: Match each part of the machine to the corresponding number.

1. _____
2. _____
3. _____
4. _____
5. _____
6. _____
7. _____
8. _____
9. _____
10. _____
11. _____
12. _____
13. _____
14. _____
15. _____
16. _____
17. _____
18. _____
19. _____
20. _____
21. _____
22. _____
23. _____
24. _____
25. _____

Clothing and Textiles

Name   Date   Period   Score

Objective: Match appropriate answers. **(Reading)**

PARTS OF THE ELNA SEWING MACHINE

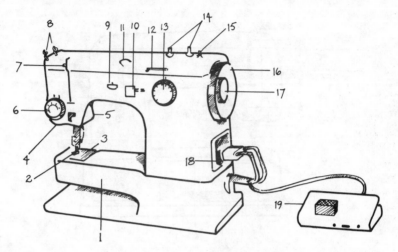

Automatic stitch selector dial	Reverse lever
Bobbin winder spindle	Rotary hook cover
Flywheel (handwheel)	Sewing foot
Flywheel (handwheel) release (coupling wheel)	Spool pins
Foot control	Stitch length regulator
Free arm	Stitch width knob
Light	Thread guides
Light switch	Thread take-up lever
Needle-position wheel	Upper thread tension dial
Presser foot lever (behind machine)	

Directions: Match each part of the machine to the corresponding number.

1. _____   11. _____

2. _____   12. _____

3. _____   13. _____

4. _____   14. _____

5. _____   15. _____

6. _____   16. _____

7. _____   17. _____

8. _____   18. _____

9. _____   19. _____

10. _____

Clothing and Textiles

Name _____ Date _____ Period _____ Score _____

Objective: Match appropriate answers. **(Reading)**

PARTS OF THE SINGER SEWING MACHINE

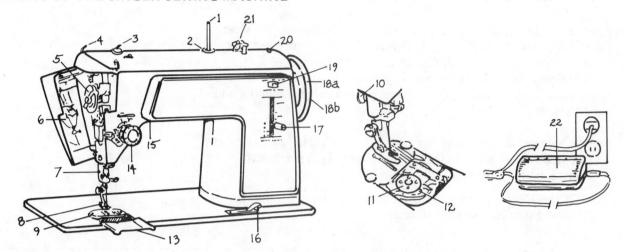

Bobbin	Pressure regulating dial
Bobbin case tension screw	Slide plate
Bobbin winder latch and spindle	Spool pin
Bobbin winder tension discs	Spool pin felt
Bobbin winder thread post	Stitch length regulator
Electrical connections and speed controller	Stop-motion nut (coupling or handwheel release)
Handwheel (flywheel)	Take-up lever
Light	Thread cutter
Needle (throat) plate	Thread tension dial
Power and light switch	Threading chart
Presser foot	Throat plate position lever
Presser foot lever	

Directions: Match each part of the machine to the corresponding number.

1. _____
2. _____
3. _____
4. _____
5. _____
6. _____
7. _____
8. _____
9. _____
10. _____
11. _____
12. _____

13. _____
14. _____
15. _____
16. _____
17. _____
18a. _____
18b. _____
19. _____
20. _____
21. _____
22. _____

Clothing and Textiles

Name   Date   Period   Score

Objective: Write objective accounts of experiences. **(Writing)**

PEER PRESSURE AND YOUR CLOTHES

Whether we like it or not, people judge us by the clothes we wear. They will check to see if we look clean and neat, are dressed in a popular style, and if our clothes enhance our appearance.

    Directions: Read the following situations. Describe your thoughts about each story. Use complete sentences, and correct spelling and punctuation.

1. Dan received a shirt from his mother as a gift. He can't stand the way it looks on him! He feels he must wear it at least once so he won't hurt his mother's feelings.

   a. If this happened to you, where would you wear it and why would you choose that place?

      _____

      _____

      _____

   b. What would you do with the shirt after wearing it, so you wouldn't make your mother feel sorry that she gave it to you?

      _____

      _____

      _____

2. All of your friends already have expensive designer jeans, and they keep asking you when you're going to buy a pair. You don't like the way you look in any of the designer jeans you've tried on. A cousin across town has invited you to spend the weekend, and you want to go. What will you say to your friends so they understand that you would rather spend the money on a weekend trip than on a pair of $40.00 jeans?

   _____

   _____

   _____

   _____

   _____

Clothing and Textiles

Name   Date   Period   Score

Objective: Write advertising copy, using sensory words. **(Writing)**

WRITING AN ADVERTISEMENT

Sandy has decided to earn extra money by using her sewing skills. Sandy wants to advertise in the school paper. She needs an ad that will attract attention and provide her with her first customers.

Directions: Compose an ad for Sandy. Be sure to include the following:

- Name
- Phone number
- Hours available

- Fees
- Sandy's schedule
- Suggested services

The following are some suggested services which Sandy might offer:

- Hems: straight skirt or pants
- Hems: full skirt, or lined skirt or pants
- Buttons: sew on or replace
- Pockets: repair or sew in new pockets
- Seams: repair torn seams or zigzag raveling edges
- Zippers: restitch or replace
- Athletic letters or emblems: sew on
- Sew complete drill team or pep club uniforms

Remember the following in creating a good advertisement for Sandy:

- The ad must be clear and give all information.
- Sandy will be charged by the *line,* and so the message must be kept fairly short; do not use extra words.

Clothing and Textiles

Name   Date   Period   Score

Objective: Write paragraphs of description. **(Writing)**

MY CLOTHING IMAGE

1. Check which of the following apply to you and your clothes.

   _____ Functional; easy-care; simple design; classic styles/sporty.

   _____ High-fashion; very stylish.

   _____ Looks like a lot of money was spent.

   _____ Includes some fads of the moment.

   _____ Includes special items that identify me with others in my group.

   _____ Tight fit.

   _____ Fit is easy; comfortable.

   _____ Conservative _____ In-between _____ Liberated

   _____ My parents think my clothing is fine.

   _____ My clothes are in conflict with my parents' ideas of appropriate clothes.

   _____ Accessories are important.

2. After analyzing your wardrobe, write a paragraph to state the way you feel you appear to other people.

   _____

   _____

   _____

   _____

3. Ask one or more of your classmates to analyze your appearance and what your clothing communicates to them. Write a paragraph describing what they say you communicate with your clothing.

   _____

   _____

   _____

   _____

Clothing and Textiles

MY CLOTHING IMAGE (cont.)

4. Write a third paragraph which compares what you think you communicate to others with what they say you communicate to them.

_____

_____

_____

_____

5. Write a fourth paragraph which describes the way you _wish_ to appear to others.

_____

_____

_____

_____

Use complete sentences, and correct spelling and punctuation.

Clothing and Textiles

Name   Date   Period   Score

Objective: Write a three-paragraph exposition. **(Writing)**

A WELL-GROOMED STUDENT

A well-groomed student is clean and neat. Hair is cut and well-combed. Clothes are clean, pressed and coordinated, as well as appropriate for the occasion.

Directions: In the first paragraph, describe a typical outfit of this person. In the second paragraph, describe this student's hairstyle, accessories, etc., used to enhance his or her looks. After completing the two paragraphs, write a third paragraph which states your impressions of the importance of good grooming. Use complete sentences, and correct spelling and punctuation.

_____

_____

_____

_____

_____

_____

_____

_____

_____

_____

_____

_____

_____

_____

_____

_____

_____

_____

Clothing and Textiles

Name _____ Date _____ Period _____ Score _____

Objective: Use illustrations or allusions to make a point in a narrative. **(Writing)**

FASHION SHOW COMMENTARY

Directions: The garment you are sewing is one you will model in the school's Spring Fashion Show. Write your own commentary for this garment. Use your imagination, if necessary, to describe other garments or accessories that you'd like to wear with this garment. Make the commentary sound so interesting that everyone in the audience will want to listen. Remember to use complete sentences, and correct spelling and punctuation. Practice reading your commentary.

_____

_____

_____

_____

_____

_____

_____

_____

_____

_____

_____

_____

_____

_____

_____

_____

_____

_____

_____

_____

_____

Clothing and Textiles

Name _____ Date _____ Period _____ Score _____

Objectives: Write a self-evaluation; compute the elapsed time in a given situation. **(Writing; Math)**

HOW I USE TIME IN CLOTHING CLASS

Directions: At the end of each day, for one week, record what you accomplished during the clothing class period.

DAY	WHAT I ACCOMPLISHED	MINUTES SPENT
MONDAY		
TUESDAY		
WEDNESDAY		
THURSDAY		
FRIDAY		

Evaluation:

A. I can accomplish more each period if I

1. _____

   _____

2. _____

   _____

3. _____

   _____

B. Problems I faced that prevented me from accomplishing things.

1. _____

2. _____

3. _____

Clothing and Textiles

Objectives: Write a self-evaluation. **(Writing)**

HOW I *WILL* USE TIME IN CLOTHING CLASS

Directions: On the following chart, list what you hope to accomplish next week each day in the clothing class period. (An alternate assignment: If you could live the past week over, what would you have tried to finish each day?)

DAY	WHAT I PLAN TO DO NEXT WEEK
MONDAY	
TUESDAY	
WEDNESDAY	
THURSDAY	
FRIDAY	

Evaluation:

A. In comparison to what I did last week, I feel that this week I

    1. _____

    _____

    2. _____

    _____

    3. _____

    _____

B. Problems I faced that prevented me from accomplishing my goals.

    1. _____

    2. _____

    3. _____

Clothing and Textiles

Name   Date   Period   Score

Objective: Calculate the sums and differences of several quantities of money. **(Math)**

WHAT'S THE BEST BUY?

Pat wanted to purchase some clothing. He looked in the newspaper for sales. Here are the prices at three stores.

ITEMS	STORE A	STORE B	STORE C
SOCKS	3 for $1.98	$.69 pair	$.99 pair
PANTS	$20.99	2 for $40	$21.59
POLO SHIRT	$17.95	$16.99	$12.25
WALLET	$11.98	$12.95	$10.49

Directions: Circle the letter of the best answer for each question.

1. Which store has the best price on socks?

   a. Store A

   b. Store B

   c. Store C

2. What is the difference in price between the highest and the lowest price polo shirts?

   a. $6.99

   b. $3.25

   c. $5.70

3. Pat works 2 hours a day and earns $8.00. How many days does he have to work to buy 2 pairs of pants at Store B?

   a. 5 days

   b. 20 days

   c. 8 days

4. How much will it cost Pat to buy 3 pairs of socks from Store A, 1 pair of pants from Store A, 1 polo shirt from Store C, and a wallet from Store C?

   a. $20.99

   b. $45.71

   c. $46.32

Clothing and Textiles

Objective: Compute linear measurements and use fractions. **(Math)**

RECOGNIZING MEASUREMENTS

A. Measure the following lines with your ruler or tape measure.
   Write the correct length in the parentheses.

1. (   ) L_____J

2. (   ) L_____J

3. (   ) L_____J

4. (   ) L__J

5. (   ) L_____J

6. (   ) L_____J

7. (   ) L_____J

8. (   ) L_____J

9. (   ) L_____J

10. (   ) L_____J

B. Measure the following amounts with your ruler or tape measure.
   Mark the length on the given lines.

   Example: 1⅛″ L_____|_____

1. ⅝″ L_____

2. 2½″ L_____

3. ¼″ L_____

4. ½″ L_____

5. 1″ L_____

6. ⅜″ L_____

7. 1½″ L_____

8. 2¾″ L_____

9. 3³⁄₁₆″ L_____

10. ⅞″ L_____

Clothing and Textiles

Name ______________________ Date ________ Period ________ Score ________

Objective: Illustrate knowledge and understanding of fractions. **(Math)**

FRACTIONS IN THE CLOTHING CLASS

Directions: Sewing requires the use of many measurements, including fractions. Please answer the following questions in the spaces provided.

______________ 1. Which is smaller: 5/8" or 1/2"?

______________ 2. Which seam allowance is larger: 3/8" or 5/8"?

______________ 3. Which is smaller: 1 1/2" or 1/2"?

______________ 4. Which of these fractions is the same as 1/2": 6/8" or 4/8"?

______________ 5. Which is smaller: 7/8" or 1"?

______________ 6. Which is larger: 2 1/2 yards or 2 3/4 yards?

A sample four-inch ruler is drawn below. On it, draw arrows which point to the positions of the following measurements.

1 1/2"	3/8"	1 1/4"	3 3/8"
1/4"	5/8"	2 1/2"	1/8"

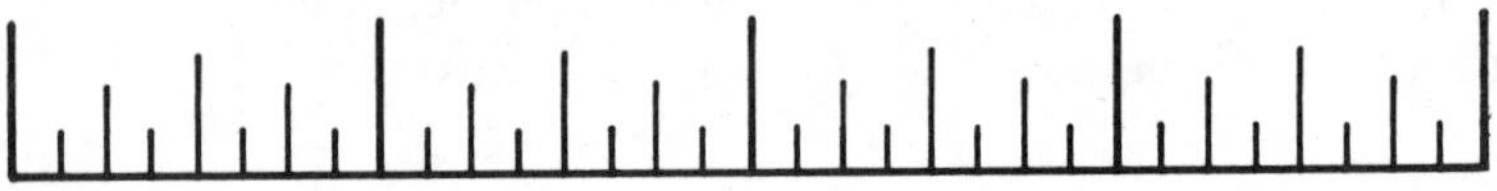

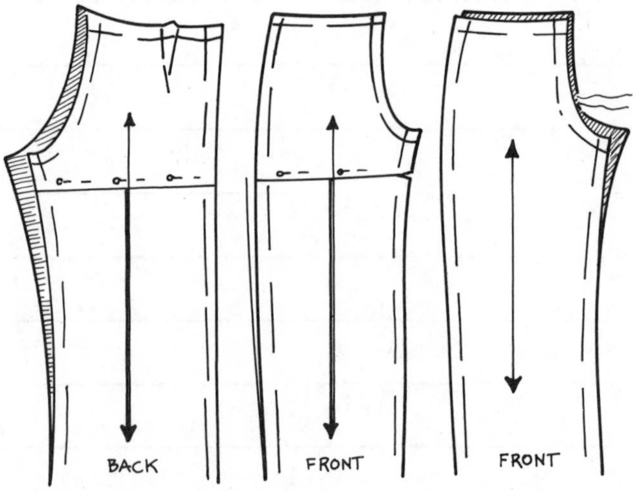

Clothing and Textiles

Name   Date   Period   Score

Objective: Compute the total cost of several units from one unit. **(Math)**

HOW MUCH WILL IT COST?

Each student in a beginning clothing class must buy materials for a first project as follows:

     Fabric — 1½ yards of 45″ denim at $2.49 yard
     Thread — 1   .59 spool
     Zipper — 1   .79 each

A kit is available with the above items for $3.25.

Directions: Circle the correct answers to the following questions.

1. How much would the materials cost if each student purchased all 3 items?

   a. $4.87
   b. 3.87
   c. 5.12
   d. 2.95

2. If a student paid full price for the materials plus the 6% sales tax, the price would be:

   a. $4.87
   b. 4.81
   c. 4.10
   d. 5.43

3. If 2 students purchased the individual items together, received a 10% discount, and paid 6% tax their total bill would be:

   a. $6.58
   b. 7.39
   c. 8.76
   d. 9.77

4. If a 10% discount were offered on individually purchased items, how much would a student pay, including 6% sales tax?

   a. $4.13
   b. 4.89
   c. 3.26
   d. 3.48

5. If 2 students purchased kits together, the total purchase price, including 6% sales tax, would be:

   a. $6.89
   b. 7.51
   c. 9.72
   d. 7.80

Clothing and Textiles

Objective: Add numbers, regrouping if necessary. **(Math)**

BUYING NOTIONS

Below is a list of supplies that one may need in the clothing class.

1.	tape measure	$ .59	10.	pinking shears	$10.00
2.	thimble	.39	11.	thread clipper	5.50
3.	seam ripper	1.00	12.	wrist pincushion	.79
4.	tracing wheel	1.29	13.	pincushion	1.19
5.	seam gauge	.79	14.	small scissors	4.00
6.	needles	.29	15.	thread	.95
7.	pins	1.25	16.	dressmaker chalk	1.25
8.	buttonhole scissors	5.50	17.	dressmaker pencil	.79
9.	shears	7.95			

Directions: Circle the letter of the correct answer.

1. The total cost of items 1–9
   would be:

   a. $16.50

   b. $18.05

   c. $19.05

   d. $17.05

2. The cost of pinking shears,
   buttonhole scissors, and
   needles would be:

   a. $14.97

   b. $13.09

   c. $15.79

   d. $15.85

3. The total cost of all items
   listed is:

   a. $34.12

   b. $43.52

   c. $41.25

   d. $45.00

4. If you purchased all the items
   on the list, what would be the
   6% sales tax?

   a. $2.61

   b. $2.65

   c. $3.00

   d. $1.50

Clothing and Textiles

Name _____ Date _____ Period _____ Score _____

Objective: Illustrate the use of math in everyday life. **(Math)**

NEEDLEPOINT PILLOWS: HOW MUCH DO THEY COST?

A sewing class has decided to buy all their supplies together. Thirty-six-inch-wide needlepoint canvas is $4.39 per yard. One skein of yarn costs $1.39.

Directions: Please answer the questions in the spaces provided below. Round off your answers to the nearest penny.

1. How many canvas pillow fronts can be made from 1 yard if each pillow measures 18″ × 18″? _____

2. How much will each pillow front cost? $_____

3. How much will it cost for pillow fronts for a class of 30 students? $_____

4. If it takes 4¼ skeins of yarn for each pillow, how much would the yarn cost for each pillow? $_____

5. What would be the total cost of 1 pillow front and the yarn for an 18″ × 18″ pillow? $_____

6. How many pillow fronts can be made from 1 yard if each front measures 12″ × 12″? $_____

7. How much will it cost for pillow fronts for a class of 30 students if each pillow measures 12″ × 12″? $_____

8. If it takes 3½ skeins of yarn for each 12″ × 12″ pillow, how much would the yarn cost for 1 pillow? $_____

9. What would be the total cost of 1 pillow front and the yarn for a 12″ × 12″ pillow? $_____

Clothing and Textiles

Name _____ Date _____ Period _____ Score _____

Objectives: Calculate the sums and differences of several quantities of money; write a paragraph that develops an opinion supported by specific facts. **(Math; Writing)**

HOW MUCH CAN YOU SAVE BY SEWING?

Sewing can be a wonderful expression of your creativity as well as an opportunity to save money. However, there are a variety of factors which need to be considered when deciding whether or not to sew a garment, over and beyond actual price.

1. Will the item you sew be comparable in looks, fit, and quality with an item you can buy?
2. How much time will it take to sew, and at what dollar rate do you value your time?
3. Could you make more money by doing something else for wages during the time you spend sewing?
4. Can the same item be purchased on sale (discount) for less than it would cost you to make it?
5. Is sewing a satisfying hobby for you?

Directions: Complete the following exercise to help you determine whether or not it will be worth your time to sew a pair of wool pants which you can buy for $52.95, including 6% sales tax.

COST ANALYSIS FOR MATERIALS

2 yds wool, $12.95 yd.	$25.90
1 spool thread	.50
1 zipper	.75
⅛ yd. interfacing	.25
1 hook and eye	.10
	$27.50
	1.65 Tax
	$29.15

EXERCISE

It will take you 3 hours to sew the pants. If your time is worth $3.95 an hour (you could earn that working), what is the total value of your time?

$_____

Cost of materials for pants	$29.15
Dollar value of your time	$_____
Cost to you to sew pants	$_____
Cost to buy pants	$52.95
Cost to sew pants	$_____
Difference	$_____

Would you consider it worth your time to sew the pants? Yes _____ No _____
Why or why not?

_____

_____

Clothing and Textiles

Name _____ Date _____ Period _____ Score _____

Objective: Compute elapsed time in a given situation. **(Math)**

HOW LONG DOES IT TAKE?

A student plans to make 12 vests for the cheerleaders at his school.
In order to plan the fee he will charge, he must know how much
time it will take him to complete 1 vest. Study the time schedule
and solve the problems.

```
TIME SCHEDULE

Lay out pattern on fabric . . . . . . . . . . . . . . . . . .   9:00— 9:15 a.m.
Cut vest . . . . . . . . . . . . . . . . . . . . . . . . . . .  9:15— 9:25
Mark and pin vest . . . . . . . . . . . . . . . . . . . . . .  9:25— 9:35
Sew and press major areas . . . . . . . . . . . . . . . . . .  9:35— 9:45
Attach facings and stitch . . . . . . . . . . . . . . . . . .  9:45—10:15
Trim, clip, turn, and understitch facings . . . . . . . . . . 10:15—10:30
Make buttonholes . . . . . . . . . . . . . . . . . . . . . .  10:30—10:50
Attach buttons . . . . . . . . . . . . . . . . . . . . . . .  10:50—11:05
Final pressing . . . . . . . . . . . . . . . . . . . . . . .  11:05—11:10
```

Directions: Circle the letter of the best answer to each question.

1. From start to finish, the
   vest took:

   a. 110 minutes

   b. 130 minutes

   c. 90 minutes

   d. 60 minutes

2. How long did it take to lay
   out, cut, mark, and pin vest?

   a. 75 minutes

   b. 35 minutes

   c. 45 minutes

   d. 60 minutes

3. If he had started 20 minutes
   earlier, at what time would
   he have finished?

   a. 11:45 a.m.

   b. 11:35 a.m.

   c. 10:50 a.m.

   d. 12:25 a.m.

4. How much longer did it take
   to do the last 6 steps than to
   do the first 3 steps?

   a. 65 minutes

   b. 85 minutes

   c. 95 minutes

   d. 60 minutes

Clothing and Textiles

Name _____ Date _____ Period _____ Score _____

Objective: Compute the yardage of vests and the cost of making them. **(Math)**

THE COST OF MAKING VESTS (I)

Your class has volunteered to make 36 red vests to be worn by
FHA-HERO Chapter members at your school. You will be making:

10 in size small
18 in size medium
 8 in size large

Directions: Please calculate the answers to the questions.

Yardage Required	*small*	*medium*	*large*
44 inch wide fabric	1 yd.	1½ yds	1¾ yds
58 inch wide fabric	¾ yds	1 yd.	1¼ yds

1. How much 44″ fabric is needed for all the small vests? _____ yards

2. How much 44″ fabric is needed for all the medium vests? _____ yards

3. How much 44″ fabric is needed for all the large vests? _____ yards

4. How much 44″ fabric is needed for all 36 vests? _____ yards

5. How much 58″ fabric is needed for the 10 small vests? _____ yards

6. How much 58″ fabric is needed for the 18 medium vests? _____ yards

7. How much 58″ fabric is needed for the 8 large vests? _____ yards

8. How much 58″ fabric is needed for all 36 vests? _____ yards

In shopping for fabric, the buyer found there were many prices
for red fabric. After checking for quality, the buyer considered
the following four fabrics:

Store A   44″ fabric: $3.98/yard   58″ fabric: $4.79/yard
Store B   44″ fabric: $3.49/yard   58″ fabric: $4.99/yard

9. How much would the 10 small vests cost at Store A in 44″ fabric? $_____

10. How much would the 10 small vests cost at Store B in 44″ fabric? $_____

11. How much would be saved by shopping at Store B for the 44″ fabric? $_____

12. How much would it cost to buy the 44″ fabric for all 36 vests at
Store B? $_____

13. How much would it cost to buy the 58″ fabric for all 36 vests at
Store A? $_____

14. What is the *difference* in cost between buying the 44″ fabric at
Store B and the 58″ fabric at Store A? $_____

Clothing and Textiles

Name   Date   Period   Score

Objective: Compute the cost of foldover binding needed for making vests. **(Math)**

THE COST OF MAKING VESTS (II)

Foldover Binding Needed

Each vest needs foldover binding to finish the raw edges. It costs 79¢/yard.

   Small: 3 yards   Medium: 3½ yards   Large: 4 yards

15. How much would the binding cost for 1 small vest? $_____

16. How much would the binding cost for 1 medium vest? $_____

17. How much would the binding cost for 1 large vest? $_____

18. How much would the binding cost for 10 small vests? $_____

19. How much would the binding cost for 18 medium vests? $_____

20. How much would the binding cost for 8 large vests? $_____

21. What is the total cost of the binding for all 36 vests? $_____

22. Calculate the cost of all 36 vests, including fabric (58″ at Store A) and binding. $_____

23. Calculate 6% sales tax on the cost. $_____

24. What is the total that needs to be spent for 36 vests? $_____

25. How much is the average cost of 1 vest? $_____

Clothing and Textiles

Name   Date   Period   Score

Objectives: Use mathematics to organize an approach to problem solving; write paragraphs of simple exposition. **(Math, Writing)**

ALTERATIONS: WILL THEY PAY?

You have been in clothing classes in both junior and senior high school. You have done very well, and you have recently altered hem lengths of skirts and pants for several of your relatives. You realize you can earn money by doing alterations for other people.

Starting a small business does require *starting capital* for equipment and supplies. Some of the things you need are already in your home. You need to comparison shop for some items to decide whether or not it would be worth your time and money to begin an alteration service.

Directions: Find out the cost of all the items in the Items You Need to Buy columns.

Items You Have at Home

Sewing machine	Seam ripper
Ironing board with pad and cover	Some assorted thread
Hand-sewing needles	Yardstick
Pincushion	Tailor's chalk

Items You Need to Buy

A. *Item*	*Est. Cost*	B. *Item*	*Est. Cost*
Steam iron	$_____	Sewing machine needles—12 each	
		Size 9	$_____
1 gal. distilled water	$_____	Size 11	$_____
Press cloth	$_____	Size 14	$_____
Pressing hem	$_____	Size 16	$_____
Hem marker	$_____	Tape measure	$_____
20 spools of thread (assorted colors)	$_____	Cutting shears (high quality)	$_____
		Pinking shears	$_____
SUBTOTAL A .... $_____			
SUBTOTAL B .... $_____		SUBTOTAL B .... $_____	
GRAND TOTAL ...... $_____		Estimated dollar start-up costs.	

Clothing and Textiles

ALTERATIONS: WILL THEY PAY? (cont.)

Please answer the following questions in the space provided:

1. If you had to purchase a better sewing machine, where might you look for a used machine?

_____

_____

_____

2. How could you determine what to charge for various types of alterations? (Remember, you will need to buy extra supplies as you use up the originals!)

_____

_____

_____

Optional

Interview two people who do alterations. Ask them what they charge for specific work and how they determined the prices. Write your findings here.

_____

_____

_____

_____

_____

_____

CONSUMER EDUCATION AND INDEPENDENT LIVING

Teacher-Managed Reading Activities

BUILDING VOCABULARY

Jeopardy

The purpose of this game is to test the student's ability to recognize descriptions and definitions of words from the Consumer Education and Independent Living Vocabulary List.

Put each word from the vocabulary list on a 3" x 5" card and list 4 definitions or descriptions of the word. Divide the class into 2 teams.

To begin: Read clue #1 (definition #1) to Side 1. Allow the side 30 seconds to identify the word. If the team identifies the word after the first clue, they receive 20 points. If their guess is incorrect, give clue #2 to Side 2. They score 15 points if their answer is correct. If their answer is incorrect, then clue #3 is given to Side 1 for 10 points. If clue #4 is given, the team scores 5 points.

The team with the highest score wins the game.

IMPROVING COMPREHENSION

1. Sequencing

Have students arrange consumer information in sequence:

a. In expository order

- cause to effect
- effect to cause
- details to general (inductive)
- general to details (deductive)

b. In alphabetical order
c. In numerical order

(*Literal Comprehension*)

2. Analyzing Advertisements

Have students read advertisements for consumer products and determine what the advertising jargon is really saying. (*Analytical Comprehension*)

3. Lodging a Complaint

Give students consumer complaint case studies and have them determine what the most logical thing to do would be. (*Applicative Comprehension*)

4. Stereotyping

Have students examine advertisements and determine what stereotypical group is generally used to advertise the following consumer products:

- Detergent
- Soft drinks
- Baking ingredients
- Beer
- Fast food restaurants
- Lawn equipment

(*Analytical Comprehension*)

LOCATION-STUDY SKILLS

Plan exercises to give students practice in locating information in or on:

- Yellow pages of the telephone directory
- Telephone directory index pages
- Textbook index pages
- Appendixes in textbooks
- Foreword in textbooks
- Newspapers and magazine advertisements relating to subject studies
- Public service organization brochures, etc.
- TV schedule
- Highway maps
- Freeway and street maps
- Telephone area-code map
- Post office ZIP-code book
- Motor vehicle driver instruction publication
- Warranties and guarantees

CONSUMER EDUCATION AND INDEPENDENT LIVING
Teacher-Managed Writing Activities

JOURNAL WRITING
(Refer to Appendix 1.)

In the sensory/descriptive domain, have students write the following
journal entries:

- When I think of living on my own, I . . .
- When I go shopping, I . . .
- The purchases I make are . . .
- Advertisements make me . . .

WRITING FILMSTRIPS
(Refer to Appendixes 2–4.)

Write filmstrip scripts in the narrative domain on the following
topics:

- Finding an apartment
- Living with a roommate
- Buying a stereo

LETTER TO THE EDITOR
(Refer to Appendix 5.)

Write a letter for the editorial section of a community or school
newspaper on the following topics:

- Shoplifting costs to the consumer
- Consumer responsibilities
- The advertising war

DRAWING MAPS/READING AND FOLLOWING MAPS
(Refer to Appendixes 11–12.)

1. Write directions for going to your nearest shopping mall,
   starting from your home.
2. Draw a map for going to your shopping mall, starting from
   your home.

CONSUMER BUSINESS LETTER
(Refer to Appendix 6.)

Write a consumer complaint letter to a store or manufacturer
about an inferior product or service, and request redress.

WRITING LISTS
(Refer to Appendix 13.)

1. List the steps to follow to balance a checkbook.
2. List the steps in determining a budget, based on personal and/or family needs and wants.

CONSUMER EDUCATION AND INDEPENDENT LIVING

Vocabulary List

abundance
advertisement
affidavit
agent
allocation
allowance
alternative
annual percentage rate
application
assets
attachment

balance
balanced budget
balloon payment
beneficiary
bill
biodegradable
blackout/brownout
borrower
budget
Bureau of Labor
  Statistics
buyer

capital
carrying charges
cash value
caveat emptor
character reference
charge account
claim
coal
collateral
compensation
competition
conservation
consumer
consumer price index
convenience
contingency basis
contract
co-signer
cost of living
credit
credit application
credit rating
credit union
creditor
crisis
currency

current
customer

debtor
decibel
deductions
default
deferred payment
delinquent
demand
dependents
deposit
depression
disclosure statement
disposable dividends
dividends
domestic
down payment
dun

ecological
ecology
economy
electricity
endorsement
energy
environment
evaluate
exemptions
expenditure
export

face amount
FICA
finance charge
fixed expense
fixture
flexible expenses
fluorescent
foreclosure
foreign
fossil fuels
fraud
free enterprise
fuel

garnishment
geothermal
goods
grace period
gross national product

gross pay
guarantee

hydroelectric

import
incandescent
income
income tax
installment
insulate
insulation
insured
interest

kilowatt

landlord
lease
lender
liability
life style
loan

media
minor
money
mortgage

natural resources
net pay
non-biodegradable
nuclear

offshore drilling

payment
petroleum
policy
pollution
power failure
premium
price
principal
priority
production
profit
promissory note
propaganda
protection
purchase

rationing
receipt
recession
recycle
repossession
resources
retail

scarcity
secured loan
service charge
services
social security
solar
standard of living
state income tax
status symbol
strip mining
summons
supply

tenant
thermal units
title
trade-in

unpaid balance
usury

voltage

waste

weatherstripping

CONSUMER EDUCATION AND INDEPENDENT LIVING

Student Worksheets—Teaching Strategies

The answers for the Consumer Education and Independent Living student worksheets
are found in the Answer Key, p. 227. Teaching strategies for selected student worksheets
are found below.

UNDERSTANDING A WATER AND POWER BILL

Students have a chance to read a genuine DWP statement and answer
questions. The bill and Conservation Information Statement can be
made into an overhead transparency if desired. Depending on the
skill level of students, they will need more or less direction in finding
the answers to their questions.

USING UTILITY BILL CUSTOMER INFORMATION

Students will need more or less help in answering the questions. It
may be interesting to have each of the meters drawn on large posters
so it is easy to see how the meters move. Students could practice
reading these meters. If feasible, students should read their meters
at home.

READING A GRAPH

Demonstrate how to solve each problem by writing the parts on the
chalkboard. Drill on other similar problems will be helpful.

1. $\begin{array}{r} \$95,000 \ (1980) \\ -20,000 \ (1950) \\ \hline \$75,000 \ \text{difference} \end{array}$

2. 1950–1960   1960–1970   1970–1980

$\begin{array}{r} \$25,000 \\ -20,000 \\ \hline \$5,000 \ \text{increase} \end{array}$	$\begin{array}{r} \$30,000 \\ -25,000 \\ \hline \$5,000 \end{array}$	$\begin{array}{r} \$95,000 \\ -30,000 \\ \hline \$65,000 \ \text{greatest difference!} \end{array}$

3. $\begin{array}{r} \$100,000 \ \text{home} \\ \times.20 \ (20\% \ \text{down payment}) \\ \hline 20,000.00 \ \text{Amount of down payment} \end{array}$

$\begin{array}{r} \$100,000 \\ -20,000 \\ \hline \$80,000 \ \text{Balance to pay} \end{array}$

4. $\dfrac{\$95,000 \ (1980 \ \text{costs})}{\$20,000 \ (1950 \ \text{costs})} = 4.75 \ \text{or} \ 475\% \ \text{increase in cost}$

BUYING SPORTS EQUIPMENT

This word problem exercise may be very difficult for some students.
A review of key techniques and a practice/scribble sheet may make
it easier to complete.

Examples:

1. Jacket $ 58.00
    Pants   39.00
    Mitts   19.00
                       $ 116.00

2. Ski Sweater $ 49.00
       (tax) $\times$.06
    (change 6% to .06) $ 2.9400

3. Sweater $ 49.00 $ 178.00
    Skis   +129.00   .06 tax
                $ 178.00   10.68 00

                $ 178.00
                +10.68 tax
                $ 188.68 Total

4. Mitts $ 19.00 $ 19.00 $ 25.00
                $\times$.06 tax   +1.14 tax   −20.14
                $ 1.1400 $ 20.14 total $ 4.86 change

5. Ski Masks $ 14.00 $ 21.00 $ 50.00
    Hat   +7.00   +1.26 tax   −22.26
                $ 21.00 $ 22.26 total $ 27.74 change
                $\times$.06 tax
                $ 1.26 00

6. Sweater $ 49.00 $ 70.00
    Goggles   14.00   +4.20 tax
    Mask   7.00 $ 74.20 total
                $ 70.00
                $\times$.06 tax
                $ 4.20 00

       $ 50 $ 100.00
       $\times$ 2 (bills)   −74.20
       $ 100 $ 25.80 change

THE HIGH COST OF SHOPLIFTING

Before assigning this lesson, the students can view *Shoplifting, It's a Steal,*
or the slides *Shoplifting.*
    The problems for this exercise can be worked on together as a class, or
by individual students if ability is high enough.

Answers and Solutions to Problems

1. $84.50 (multiply unit by number of items lost)

2. $21.00 new price   20 Sweaters must be sold at $21.00 to
  20.00 old price $1)$20 recover $20.00.
  $ 1.00 increase

3. 2 necklaces at $5.00 = $10.00 loss.

  new price $6.00   10   necklaces must be sold at $6.00 to
  old price   5.00 $1)$10.00   recover $10.00.
             $1.00 increase

4. 8 cosmetics at $2.50 = $20.00 loss

  $\dfrac{\$20.00 \text{ lost}}{40 \quad \text{to be sold}}$ = $.50 Amount that needs to be added to each cosmetic

  $2.50 original price
  +.50 price increase needed
  $3.00 new retail price

5. $18.00

6. a. 2 scarves at $4.00 = $8.00 loss

    $\dfrac{\$8.00 \text{ loss}}{\$ .25 \text{ increase}}$ = 32 scarves need to be sold at $4.25 to
                 recover the $8.00 loss.

  b. 5 cards at $.80 = $4.00 loss

    $\dfrac{\$4.00 \text{ loss}}{\$ .25 \text{ increase}}$ = 16 cards need to be sold at $1.05 to recover
                the $4.00 loss.

  c. 1 frame at $6.00 loss

    $\dfrac{\$6.00 \text{ loss}}{\$ .25 \text{ increase}}$ = 24 frames need to be sold at $6.25 to recover
                the $6.00 loss.

  d. 32 scarves
    +16 cards
    +24 frames
      72

    72 *items* would need to be sold at a 25¢ increase to recover
      the $18.00 total loss.

7. $ 2.40 unit price increase
   5,000)$12,000.00

8. $15,000 worth of merchandise recovered
   <u> 12,000</u> salary
   $ 3,000 saved by store

9. customer

10. bankruptcy

Consumer Education and Independent Living

Name _____ Date _____ Period _____ Score _____

Objective: Identify reliability and validity of information. **(Reading)**

GUARANTEE

GUARANTEE

The Soft Tone Stereo Corporation guarantees to the buyer that each part of this stereo is free from defective materials and defective workmanship for one full year from date of purchase. All necessary repairs will be made by contacting the nearest factory-authorized service center. All service, including parts and labor, will be performed free of charge to the buyer, during the term of the guarantee.

This guarantee does not include replacement of the needle cartridge, nor does it include damage caused by incorrect use or carelessness.

There is no guarantee, expressed or implied, made by the Soft Tone Stereo Corporation of Toledo, Ohio, except the above direct guarantee.

Directions: Read the above guarantee. Circle the letter of the best answer for each question about the guarantee.

1. The guarantee is good for

   a. 6 months   c. 2 months
   b. 12 months   d. 24 months

2. To have the stereo repaired at company expense, you must

   a. return to store where purchased
   b. return to the Soft Tone Corporation in Ohio
   c. take it to a neighborhood repair shop
   d. contact a factory-authorized repair center

3. Which of the following is NOT covered by the guarantee?

   a. the needle cartridge
   b. the dial
   c. the arm
   d. the speaker

4. A more complete guarantee

   a. is available at the store
   b. can be requested from the corporation
   c. can be requested from the factory-authorized repair center
   d. does not exist

5. The guarantee covers

   a. defective materials
   b. defective workmanship
   c. both of the above
   d. neither of the above

Consumer Education and Independent Living

Name _____ Date _____ Period _____ Score _____

Objective: Follow written directions to complete specific tasks. **(Reading)**

BANK CHECKING ACCOUNT APPLICATION

Directions: The form below is similar to one to be filled out when applying for a checking account at a bank. Complete this application/signature card with as much information as possible. Use your own name and address.

APPLICATION

_____ No. _____
(Type or print name of depositor here)

The undersigned depositor agrees with Liberty National Bank that this account is to be carried by said bank as a CHECKING SAVINGS account and all funds which the undersigned depositor has or may have on deposit therein with said bank shall be governed by its by-laws, all future amendments thereof, all regulations passed or hereafter to be passed by its Board of Directors pursuant to said by-laws, and by all rules and practices of said bank relating thereto including interest, service charges, etc.

Signature Mr. Ms.
Miss Mrs. _____

Address _____ Telephone _____
Number and Street   Apt. #

_____
City   State   ZIP Code

Social Security Number _____–_____–_____ Employer _____

Birthplace _____ Mother's Maiden Name _____

- -

BANK USE ONLY

Introduced by _____ Bank Reference _____

Account Closed _____ Aver. Bal. $_____ Reason_____

Individual or Individual Trustee _____

- -

Consumer Education and Independent Living

Name _____ Date _____ Period _____ Score _____

Objective: Recognize and use context clues through examples. **(Reading)**

CAN YOU IDENTIFY THESE CONSUMER PROTECTION LAWS?

Directions: Referring to the consumer protection laws, match the law
to the situation it was designed to control.

A. Automobile Disclosure Act
B. Wool Products Labeling Act
C. Flammable Fabrics Act
D. Textile Fiber Products Identification Act
E. Fur Products Labeling Act
F. Food, Drug and Cosmetic Act

G. Fair Packaging and Labeling Act
H. Consumer Credit Protection Act
I. Child Protection Act
J. Federal Hazardous Substances Act
K. Auto Mechanics Work Law

1. _____ Sets of flannel pajamas were pulled off the shelves
of a chain store because they were flammable.

2. _____ Although the material looks and feels like silk,
Marguerite examines the label and finds it is a synthetic.

3. _____ A Pennsylvania firm that manufactures toys painted
with lead paint is not allowed to ship them to another state.

4. _____ By reading the label, you can tell if a hair-coloring
agent is permanent or will wash out in a few weeks.

5. _____ A local firm advertises and shows an auto on TV for $5,000,
but when you drive out to see it a label on the window has added $900
for accessories and states a total price of $5,900.

6. _____ A rug manufacturer saves money by buying old clothes of
a certain fiber to use in his rugs.

7. _____ Rita's new coat was advertised as "lapin," but it says
"rabbit" on the label.

8. _____ An ointment sold in interstate commerce states, "Helps
reduce sore muscle pain," instead of "Stops pain."

9. _____ Marjorie finds the loan she thought was 6 percent really
amounts to 12 percent when she figures out the dollar cost stated by
the lender.

10. _____ The label on an oven cleaner says: "Warning, harmful if
in contact with eyes or skin."

11. _____ It is all right to label olives "jumbo olives," but illegal to
label cereal a "jumbo pound."

12. _____ When selling a car on credit, the dealer is required to also
state the price if the car is not bought on credit.

13. _____ Charges for automobile repairs may not exceed the originally
quoted price, without the express permission of the person requesting the
repairs.

Consumer Education and Independent Living

Name _____ Date _____ Period _____ Score _____

Objectives: React personally to printed material; write a paragraph of personal opinion. **(Reading; Writing)**

BUYING A CAR—USING CLASSIFIED ADVERTISEMENTS

A. It may be possible to judge the character of a dealer by the advertising he or she uses. Read the following typical advertising slogans.

"Lowest prices in town."   "The greatest sale ever held."
"Name your own deal."   "We beat any deal in town."

In the classified ads in the newspaper, find other phrases such as the above which may be considered questionable. Write them in the spaces below.

Phrase #1: _____

Phrase #2: _____

Phrase #3: _____

Choose one of the above three phrases. Write your evaluation of that ad in the space below.   #1_____   #2_____   #3_____ (Check one)

_____

_____

_____

B. Find three classified ads for a car of a particular year and model with similar equipment. List the information in the spaces provided.

Make of car _____ Model _____ Year: 19____

Dealer #1 _____ Price $_____

List of equipment _____   _____

_____   _____

Dealer #2 _____ Price $_____

List of equipment _____   _____

_____   _____

Dealer #3 _____ Price $_____

List of equipment _____   _____

_____   _____

Which dealer would you buy the car from? _____

C. Below, write your *opinion* of the three cars. Indicate why you would choose one over the other. Staple the three ads to this page.

_____

_____

Consumer Education and Independent Living

Name _____ Date _____ Period _____ Score _____

Objectives: Compare and contrast information; do simple computations. **(Reading; Math)**

SHOPPING BY MAIL

Directions: Shopping by mail can be a convenient way to buy many things, from clothes to toys to tires. Read the sample catalog advertisement, and fill in the *order blank* according to instructions below.

A. Fill out your name and address on the sample *order blank.*

B. "Order" two medium vests filling in all correct information in the spaces provided on the order blank. Your method of payment will be by check.

> SAVE 40% on the Reversible, Quilted Vest   Now — $13.79
> MAN'S REVERSIBLE VEST. Smooth poplin shell reverses to plain pattern quilted
> flannel shell—both in polyester and cotton. Insulated with polyester fiber fill. Banded
> collar has snap closure. Zipper front closure, 2 snap-flap pockets and 2 lower welt pockets
> on poplin side; 2 welt pockets on flannel side. Camel color reverses to blue/camel plaid.
> Machine wash warm, tumble dry. Shipping wt. 1 lb. 10 oz. Reduced from our big Fall
> Catalog. Sizes: S (fits 36–38" chest), M (39–41"), L (42–44"), XL (45–46").
> State S, M, L, or XL.
> HB 516-2516 B . . . . Was $23.00   Now — $13.79

C. Add the total cost of the item you have listed on the order form. Add 6% sales tax and $1.50 for shipping and handling. You will be paying by check; indicate the *amount enclosed* in the correct blank.

> After you have completed the *order blank,* please answer the following questions.

1. What was the original price of the vest? $_____

2. What is the sale price of the vest? $_____

3. How much will you save by buying the vest on sale? $_____

4. How does the vest collar stay closed?

_____

5. What color is on the reverse side of the blue/camel plaid on the vest?

_____

6. What is the vest insulated with?

_____

Consumer Education and Independent Living

SHOPPING BY MAIL (cont.)

ORDER BLANK

AND CHANGE-OF-ADDRESS NOTICE*

PLEASE DO NOT WRITE IN ABOVE SPACE.

#1. MY PRESENT NAME, ADDRESS

Name_____
(FIRST)   (MIDDLE INITIAL)   (LAST)

Address_____ Apt. No. _____
(STREET ADDRESS OR RURAL RT.)   (OR BOX NO.)

City_____ State _____

ZIP code_____ Phone _____

#2. MY PREVIOUS ADDRESS

(Fill-in only if we do not have your CORRECT PRESENT address.)

Address_____ Apt. No._____

City_____

State_____ ZIP code_____

SHIP TO ANOTHER ADDRESS

Name_____

Address_____ Apt. No._____

City_____ State_____

ZIP code_____ Phone_____

PLEASE PRINT ALL INFORMATION   Date

METHOD OF PAYMENT

☐ PLEASE OPEN AN ACCOUNT. I am submitting the completed application form on page 486.

☐ ADD TO MY CHARG-ALL ACCOUNT

My acct. no. is: ☐☐☐-☐☐☐-☐☐☐

☐ CASH (check or money order)

☐ SPECIAL INSTRUCTIONS_____

This purchase is made at a time sale price, consisting of the cash sale price and a time price differential or finance charge and is subject to the terms and conditions of my Credit Agreement with you.

SIGNATURE   (Sign full name as shown on your account)

PLEASE NOTE:

✓ Save time . . . phone your order . . . see pages 480-481. for the   Store or Agency nearest you.

✓ Combine orders and save! Transportation costs will generally be lower. See page 482 for details.

✓ Shop the easy way—use your Charg-all! For complete credit terms see pages 485-488.

NAME OF ITEM (1 or 2 words)	COMPLETE CATALOG NUMBER	HOW MANY (Pkgs., etc.)	COLOR NUMBER	SIZE or other code number	PRICE FOR ONE (Pkg., Yd., Ea., etc.)	TOTAL PRICE	SHIP. WT. (Fill-in for cash orders only.) LBS. OZ.

TAX (subject to change by State and/or Local governments)

Arizona*: 4%; California (outside Alameda, Contra Costa, Santa Clara, and San Francisco Counties): 6%; California (within Alameda, Contra Costa, Santa Clara, and San Francisco Counties): 6½%; Nevada: 3½% (state and local).

*Add local tax, if applicable in your locality.

FILL IN FOR ALL CASH ORDERS. ON CREDIT ORDERS FIGURES THESE CHARGES.

		Total lbs.	Total oz.
TOTAL FOR GOODS			
TAX (see at left)			
Transportation and Handling		**Total wt. in lbs**	
Owed on previous cash orders			
CASH PRICE			
AMOUNT ENCLOSED	Check, Money Order	16 oz. = 1 lb. count any remaining oz. as a full lb.	
	Refund Drafts		

C.O.D. ORDERS NOT ACCEPTED

Depend on us to ship non-mailable items the best way. If you have a preference, please write it here →

REFUNDS by us are usually made by draft. If a draft is not presented for payment within one year from the date of issue, a service charge thereafter of $2 per year (but not more than the face value of the draft) will be deducted.

Consumer Education and Independent Living

Name   Date   Period   Score

Objective: Use written materials to draw conclusions and to predict outcomes. **(Reading)**

MAKE COMPLAINING COUNT (I)

You should complain whenever you feel dissatisfied with a product or service and feel that it does not live up to specific claims or reasonable expectations. Take action in this order:

1. Go directly to the store where the purchase was made. Find the correct person to whom the complaint should be made. Clearly state the facts and the expected outcome of your complaint.
2. If the merchant will not help you, write to the manufacturer. (Showing the letter to your merchant may also get action.)
3. If there has been no action within a month, send a second, firmer letter to the manufacturer, with copies to government and business agencies which are concerned with consumer problems. In the letter, list the agencies to whom you are sending copies.
4. Use the Standard Complaint Form and send it to your state's consumer affairs department. Look in the phone directory for assistance.

Helpful Hints for Complainers

1. Be sure you have read all instruction books before complaining. Be *sure* you have a legitimate complaint.
2. Before returning to the store, plan your strategy carefully. What is the problem? What do you want done about it?
3. Save all receipts, tags, wrapping, etc. when you buy something until the product has proved to be satisfactory.
4. When writing, be sure to include your name, address, and phone number. Save copies of all correspondence.
5. Allow two to three weeks for action to be taken.
6. When making a complaint in person, don't let the person with whom you are dealing dissuade you from the solution you want. Assert yourself.

Activities to Consider

1. Discuss the reasons for making complaints.
2. Discuss how you or your parents have already achieved redress on a faulty product or service.
3. Describe a typical consumer problem, such as a faulty car which the owners have not been able to *really* get fixed correctly.
4. Fill out the Standard Complaint Form, which is to be sent to your state's consumer affairs department, when there is need for redress and all other sources have been exhausted.
5. Write a consumer complaint letter.

Consumer Education and Independent Living

Name _____ Date _____ Period _____ Score _____

Objectives: Follow written directions to complete a specific task; develop a paragraph by means of chronology. **(Reading; Writing)**

MAKE COMPLAINING COUNT (II)

Standard Complaint Form
(Print or Type)

COMPLAINANT

YOUR NAME _____
First name   Middle initial   Last name

HOME ADDRESS _____
No. & Street   City and State   ZIP Code

BUSINESS ADDRESS _____
No. & Street   City and State   ZIP Code

HOME PHONE _____ BUSINESS PHONE _____

COMPLAINT AGAINST

NAME _____
(Person, Company, or Firm: Use name appearing in telephone book, if possible. If complaint involves a mobile home, list address of both dealer and manufacturer.)

ADDRESS _____
No. & Street   City and State   ZIP Code

TELEPHONE _____ SALESPERSON OR REPRESENTATIVE _____

NATURE OF COMPLAINT

DATE OF TRANSACTION _____ DID YOU COMPLAIN TO COMPANY? _____

DATE YOU COMPLAINED TO COMPANY _____

HAS A LAWSUIT BEEN FILED IN SMALL CLAIMS COURT? _____ OTHER? _____

HAVE YOU CONTACTED A PRIVATE ATTORNEY? _____

ATTORNEY'S NAME _____

ATTORNEY'S ADDRESS _____
No. & Street   City & State   ZIP Code

DOES PRODUCT HAVE SERIAL NUMBER? _____ NUMBER _____

DOES PRODUCT HAVE MODEL NUMBER? _____ NUMBER _____

WAS THE PRODUCT OR SERVICE ADVERTISED? _____ WHERE? _____

DATE OF ADVERTISEMENT _____

Describe the events as fully as you can, in the order in which they happened, using extra sheets if you need to. If the work was contracted, please attach a copy of the contract and copies of the advertisement, receipts, etc.

_____

_____

_____

_____

Consumer Education and Independent Living

MAKE COMPLAINING COUNT (II) (cont.)

_____

_____

_____

_____

_____

_____

_____

_____

_____

_____

_____

_____

_____

_____

_____

_____

_____

_____

In order to resolve your problem, this complaint may be sent to the person, company, or firm complained against.

I hereby certify that I have read the information contained in this complaint and that all the information which I have given herein is true, correct, and complete to the best of my knowledge, information, and belief.

SIGNATURE _____

DATE _____

WHEN COMPLETED

Send to your state's consumer affairs department.

Consumer Education and Independent Living

Name _____ Date _____ Period _____ Score _____

Objective: Follow written directions to complete specific tasks. **(Reading)**

RENTAL APPLICATION

Directions: Fill in the rental application below. You can make up any details that are not in your experience.

Application
(Print or Type)

Apt. No. _____ Move in Date _____ Unfurnished _____

Rented by: _____ Furnished _____

PLEASE PRINT

Driver's License: _____ Social Security No. _____

Name _____ Age _____

Spouse's Name _____ Age _____

Names of Children _____

Present Address _____ Phone_____

City _____ State _____ Length of Stay _____

Why are you vacating? _____

PREVIOUS RESIDENCE

Previous Manager's Name _____

Name of Apartments (if applicable) _____

Length of Occupancy _____ Phone_____

EMPLOYMENT

Present Employer _____ Person in Charge _____

Address _____ Phone_____

Occupation _____ How Long?_____ Salary_____

Previous Employer _____ Person in Charge _____

Address _____ Phone_____

Occupation _____ How Long?_____ Salary_____

Spouse's Employer _____ Person in Charge _____

Address _____ Phone_____

Occupation _____ How Long?_____ Salary_____

Consumer Education and Independent Living

RENTAL APPLICATION (cont.)

CREDIT REFERENCES

Bank & Branch _____ Address _____

Credit Cards

1. _____ Account No. _____

2. _____ Account No. _____

3. _____ Account No. _____

OTHER INFORMATION

Automobile _____ Year _____ License No. _____

Automobile _____ Year _____ License No. _____

Motorcycle _____ Year _____ License No. _____

Description of your pets: _____

In case of emergency, notify: _____ Relationship _____

Address _____ Phone _____

PERSONAL REFERENCES

Name _____ Phone _____

Name _____ Phone _____

Total Number of Persons to Occupy Apartment: _____

Name	*Age*	*Relationship*
_____	_____	_____
_____	_____	_____
_____	_____	_____
_____	_____	_____

EDUCATION

High School Graduate _____ Yes _____ No   College _____ Yes _____ No

Which of the following first called your attention to our Complex?

_____ Signs–Billboard	_____ Newspaper Classified
_____ Other Resident	_____ Phone Directory
_____ Employer	_____ Radio
_____ Drove By	_____ Other–Specify

Consumer Education and Independent Living

RENTAL APPLICATION (cont.)

What most influenced you to rent at this complex?

_____ Management   _____ Recreation Facilities

_____ Location   _____ General Appearance

_____ Rental Rate

How long do you intend to remain upon acceptance?

Lease 1 year _____   6 Months _____   Month to Month _____

In addition to completing this form, all prospective residents will pay an application and administrative deposit of $50 in order to be placed on the waiting list. In the event the application is turned down or is withdrawn within five (5) days, the application deposit will be fully refunded. Upon notification that the application is accepted, and an apartment is assigned and accepted, the application deposit will automatically become an earnest money deposit toward your deposit.

Applicant represents that he or she understands and agrees to the above conditions and that statements made above are true and correct, and hereby authorizes verification of information given. If this information is found to be incorrect, applicant will be automatically disqualified. In the event that something happens and occupancy cannot be on the date promised, Management of the General Partners will not be held responsible and are exempt from suit.

_____

_____   BY _____

Signature of Applicant(s)

For Apt. No. _____

FOR OFFICE USE ONLY

Verify: Past Residence _____   Employment _____

Credit_____ R.C.A. _____ Base Rent Dividend _____

By Gross Income Equals _____ per cent.

Consumer Education and Independent Living

Objective: Interpret a utility bill. **(Reading)**

WHAT DOES THIS GAS BILL TELL YOU?

```
Please bring entire bill if payment is made in person.    DETACH HERE  ACME GAS COMPANY
See other side for addresses of Company Offices
     William Bishop                    TELEPHONE   (701) 666-6666
     1531 Albion St.                        Your Account Number              Rate Schedule
     Fargo, ND 58102                    01-4557-935-6393-8                       R13
```

| BILLING PERIOD | | METER READINGS | | | BILLING | THERMS |
FROM	TO	PREVIOUS	PRESENT	DIFFERENCE	FACTOR	
FEB 01, 1980 TO MAR 04, 1980		5858	5970	112 X 1.063	=	119

```
NEXT METER READING
DATE     APR 02

CUSTOMER CHARGE                                       $     3.10
LIFELINE THERMS                    81 a $ .23446=        18.99
USAGE OVER LIFELINE:               38 a   .30140=        11.45    AMOUNT

                          CITY TAX  5%                    1.68
                          TOTAL CURRENT CHARGES                   35.22


DATE MAILED-MAR 06 1980              TOTAL AMOUNT DUE      $   35.22
```

```
      SMALL AIR LEAKS AROUND WINDOWS AND DOORS
          CAN INCREASE HOME HEATING COSTS —
                   WEATHERSTRIP
```

COMPARE YOUR AVERAGE DAILY USE WITH LAST YEAR			
BILLING PERIOD	BILLING DAYS	THERMS BILLED	DAILY AVERAGE
THIS YEAR	32	119	3.7 THERMS
LAST YEAR	32	176	5.5 THERMS

Directions: Answer the following questions to show your understanding of the above gas bill.

1. The account number for this customer's bill is _____ .

2. The billing period for this bill is from _____ to _____ .

3. The previous meter reading was _____ .

4. The present meter reading is _____ .

5. How many therms were used? _____ .

6. What is the *basic* monthly customer charge? $_____

7. Thirty-eight therms were used over the lifeline allowance. What is the difference in cost per therm between a lifeline therm and therms used over the lifeline? $_____

8. How much city tax must be paid? $_____

9. The city tax is what percent? _____ %

10. What is the difference in number of therms used between 1979 and and 1980? _____

Consumer Education and Independent Living

Name _____   Date _____   Period _____   Score _____

Objective: Interpret a utility bill. **(Reading)**

UNDERSTANDING A WATER AND POWER BILL (I)

Directions: Study the bill from the Department of Water and Power.
Answer the following questions.

1. How much is the total water and electricity bill for this
   bimonthly billing period? $_____

2. How many days are included in this bill?   _____

3. How many kilowatt hours of electricity were used?   _____

4. How many hundred cubic feet of water were used?   _____

5. A city tax is charged for electricity use. What percent
   of the electricity portion is this?   _____ %

6. How much is the sewer service charge? $_____

SERVICE ADDRESS
1531 Albion St.

ACCOUNT NUMBER
3081257815564000000000100000093801

DWP **WATER and POWER** **PLEASE KEEP THIS PORTION**
CITY OF FARGO   **FOR YOUR RECORDS**

CODE	SERVICE FROM	TO	NO. OF DAYS	METER READINGS PRESENT	PREVIOUS	KWH OR 100 CU. FT.	AMOUNT
E	11/08/79	1/11/80	64	72683	71446	1237	7524
	INCLUDES ENERGY COST OF $33.83 FOR ELECTRIC						
	STATE SURCHARGE @ $.00015 PER KWH						019
				5 PERCENT CITY TAX			376
W	11/08/79	1/11/80	64	4426	4401	25	1311
	INCLUDES			$.18 FOR PURCHASED WATER COST			
				SEWER SERVICE CHARGE			150

METER NUMBER	SERVES	CONSTANT	BILLING DEMAND	$9380
E 6-425467				
W 9262612				**TOTAL DUE**

Consumer Education and Independent Living

Name   Date   Period   Score

Objective: Interpret a utility bill. **(Reading)**

UNDERSTANDING A WATER AND POWER BILL (II)

Directions: Study the Conservation Information statement from the Department of Water and Power. The statement is found on the back of the water and power bill.

1. What is the earliest date on the statement?   _____

2. How many kilowatt hours were used from 7/12/78 to 9/11/78?   _____

3. How many kilowatt hours were used from 5/10/79 to 7/11/79?   _____

4. If there are 748 gallons in 100 cubic feet of water, how many gallons of water were used from 9/10/79 to 11/08/79?   _____

CONSERVATION INFORMATION

ELECTRIC METER NUMBER 6-425467			METER SEQUENCE 02	WATER METER NUMBER 9262612			METER SEQUENCE 01
SERVICE TO	**NO.OF DAYS**	**KILOWATT HOURS**	**KWH PER DAY**	**SERVICE TO**	**NO.OF DAYS**	**100 CU. FT.**	**GALLONS PER DAY**
1/11/80	64	1237	19	1/11/80	64	25	292
11/08/79	59	1476	25	11/08/79	59	31	393
9/10/79	61	1476	24	9/10/79	61	47	576
7/11/79	62	1361	22	7/11/79	62	47	567
5/10/79	58	1033	18	5/10/79	58	20	258
3/13/79	61	1239	20	3/13/79	61	11	135
1/11/79	122	1940	16	1/11/79	64	16	187
	00	0		11/08/78	58	36	464
9/11/78	61	2829	46	9/11/78	61	55	674
7/12/78	62	1708	28	7/12/78	62	47	567
5/11/78	58	1179	20	5/11/78	58	18	232
3/14/78	61	1367	22	3/14/78	61	11	135
1/12/78	64	1503	23	1/12/78	64	23	269

Consumer Education and Independent Living

Name _____ Date _____ Period _____ Score _____

Objective: Interpret a utility bill. **(Reading)**

USING UTILITY BILL CUSTOMER INFORMATION

Directions: Sometimes the back side of the bill from the Department of Water and Power gives you the information to answer the following questions.

1. To read the electric meter, you read the dials from _____

   to _____ , recording the last number the pointer has passed.

2. Two of the dials are read clockwise; two are read _____ .

3. 1 KWH = a _____ watt bulb burning _____ hours.

4. To read the water meter, you read only the _____ , _____

   and _____ dials.

5. One cubic foot of water equals _____ gallons.

6. A meter reading of 968 cubic feet would mean you had used _____ gallons of water.

CONSERVATION INFORMATION: 481-5800

HOW TO READ YOUR METERS

NOTE: The pointers may move in a clockwise or a counterclockwise direction.

YOUR ELECTRIC METER • Read the dials from right to left and write down, in the same order, the last number the pointer has passed. The result is your meter reading.

If the pointer is directly on a number, record the next lower number unless the pointer on the dial to the right has passed 0

THE METER ABOVE READS 4351

1 KWH = 100 Watt Bulb Burning 10 Hours

CODE 03200 REV. 9-78

HELP CONSERVE – READ YOUR METERS

DATE	ELECTRIC READ	CONSUMPTION	WATER READ	CONSUMPTION

YOUR WATER METER

The dials that show 1, 10, 100 cubic feet are used for test purposes only. Read the 1,000 cubic foot dial and continue with the 10,000 and 100,000 cubic foot dials, etc. Write down, from right to left, the last number the pointer has passed. The result is your meter reading.

If the pointer is directly on a number, record the next lower number unless the pointer on the next lower denomination dial has passed 0.

1 Cu. Ft. = 7.48 Gallons

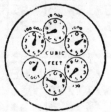

THE METER ABOVE READS 968

Extra Credit

Using the chart above, read the electric and water meters at your residence for three consecutive weeks and record your findings.
Calculate total water and electricity consumption.

Consumer Education and Independent Living

Name   Date   Period   Score

Objective: Write advertising copy, using sensory words. **(Writing)**

ADVERTISING

Directions: You have been assigned to make a poster for a school club. The club has been given permission to sell frozen, yogurt-dipped bananas during lunch in the cafeteria. The profits will go to the Special Olympics. The poster should be 8½ x 11" in size; it will be duplicated on colored paper to be posted all over campus.

Advertisements need to include the following:

1. *Information:* What, where, when, why, and for whom
2. *Appeal:* Psychological, goodwill, etc.
3. *Attractiveness*
   a. Lettering should be simple in style, and on even lines.
   b. The most important idea should be written the largest.
   c. Any pictures or drawings should look good.
   d. The words should be in "blocks" with space left around each block. This helps each idea to stand out.

What to Include on your Poster

1. Support the Special Olympics.
2. Frozen, yogurt-dipped, peanut-topped bananas.
3. Bananas are high in potassium; for your good health.
4. For sale, at lunch, in the cafeteria.
5. Sponsored by FHA–HERO.
6. Price: 50¢.
7. Dates: Oct. 3, 4, and 5

Optional Assignment

Create a poster for a different club, sponsoring a different activity. Be sure you include the same type of information given above.

Consumer Education and Independent Living

Name _____ Date _____ Period _____ Score _____

Objective: Write short paragraphs of personal opinion. **(Writing)**

THOUGHTS ABOUT CREDIT

Directions: On a separate sheet(s) of paper, write as many paragraphs as you wish to reveal your *opinion* about the statements below. When possible, support your opinion with facts.
   Use correct spelling and punctuation and correct paragraph form.

1. People used to be ashamed to use credit; now they are proud to have many sources of credit.

2. People tend to limit their use of credit to what companies will allow, not to what they can afford to spend.

3. More people are using credit just to keep even with everyday needs.

4. People forget that goods and services purchased with credit almost always cost more than if paid for in cash.

5. The use of credit reduces future income.

6. Overextended credit may cause family problems.

7. Misuse of credit may limit the quality of family life.

8. Saving in advance for a purchase may have an advantage over purchasing the item on credit.

9. A sale item purchased on credit may eventually cost more than its original price.

10. Some items must be purchased on credit because it is difficult to save enough to purchase them for cash.

11. Credit may be a great financial tool if used correctly.

Consumer Education and Independent Living

Name _____   Date _____   Period _____   Score _____

Objective: Write consumer complaint letters of a simple nature; write a paragraph of simple exposition. **(Writing)**

MY WORST SHOPPING EXPERIENCE

Your name is _____ and you are _____ years old. Your parents agreed that you need a new pair of school shoes. They gave you the money so you and your friend could go shopping after school. You visited two stores that carried the shoes you liked, and you bought a pair of athletic shoes for $29.95.

After you came home, your friend asked to try them on and as you handed him (or her) the shoes, you discovered a two-inch section where the sole was coming loose. You and your friends went back to the shoe store with your receipt, but the sales clerk refused to exchange the shoes for another pair. He said, "You wore those shoes home and must have ripped them after you left the store."

A. Explain how you would ask your parents for help in exchanging the shoes. Use complete sentences, correct spelling, and correct punctuation. Write in the space below.

_____

_____

_____

_____

_____

_____

_____

_____

_____

B. Write a letter to Mr. David Jones, the manager of the shoe store, explaining your problem and the unsatisfactory service his sales clerk has given you. Ask to be reimbursed or to have a letter from him approving a new pair of shoes. Do not send your receipt with the letter, but mention that you do have the receipt. Include your name, your parents' names, and your complete address. Use correct business letter form, and write the letter on a separate piece of paper. Mr. Jones' address:

> 821 West 79th Street
> New York, NY 10024

Consumer Education and Independent Living

Name _____ Date _____ Period _____ Score _____

Objective: Write anecdotes of personal experience and do simple calculating. **(Math, Writing)**

HOW DO YOU SPEND YOUR MONEY?

Directions: Answer the following questions in the spaces provided.

1. Source of weekly spending money:

   a. $_____ Allowance b. $_____ Job c. $_____ Other

2. What is your total weekly income? $_____

3. Listed below are some of the ways people spend money. Please estimate how much of your weekly income is used for each of these items. Be sure your total is the same as or less than your net income. (#2 above).

$_____ snack food	$_____ church/charity, etc.	$_____ food at school
_____ reading material	_____ movies/concerts/dates	_____ club dues
_____ gifts	_____ cosmetics, toiletries	_____ school supplies
_____ expenses for pet(s)	_____ transportation	_____ clothes, shoes, etc.
_____ hobbies/music, etc.	_____ repaying loans	_____ haircuts, laundry, etc.
$_____ Subtotal	_____ savings	_____ other
	$_____ Subtotal	$_____ Subtotal

   What is the total of the columns? $_____

4. Most people do not spend their money the same way every week. Please describe how your spending patterns change throughout the month.

   _____

   _____

   _____

   _____

   _____

5. Plan a simple *monthly* budget with the amount of money you have available right now. If you have *almost no money* now, plan how you would like to spend a monthly net income (the money you have left over after taxes, etc.) of $_____ . List the items you would use the money for and their estimated prices in the spaces provided.

   Net monthly income: $_____

Item	*Price*	*Item*	*Price*
_____	$_____	_____	$_____
_____	_____	_____	_____
_____	_____	_____	_____
_____	_____	_____	_____
_____	_____	_____	_____
Subtotal	$_____	Subtotal	$_____

   GRAND TOTAL $_____

6. How much is the above over or under your net monthly income? (If applicable).

   Over $_____ Under $_____

Consumer Education and Independent Living

Name _____ Date _____ Period _____ Score _____

Objective: Use mathematics to organize an approach to problem-solving. **(Math)**

COMPARATIVE PRICING

Directions: The Anderson family subscribes to a local newspaper at a cost of $8 per month. There is a savings to be realized if the Andersons subscribe on an annual basis. Study the chart and answer the questions below.

```
┌─────────────────────────────────────────────────────────┐
│                  METROPOLIS CHRONICLE                     │
│                                                           │
│                   Subscription Rates                      │
│                                                           │
│   Monthly Charge . . . . . . . . . . . . . . . . . $8.00  │
│                                                           │
│   Sunday Only . . . . . . . . . . . . . . . . .  .75/week │
│                                                           │
└─────────────────────────────────────────────────────────┘
```

1. How much will it cost the Andersons if they subscribe by the month for one year?

   a. $144.00

   b.   52.00

   c.   96.00

2. If there are 52 Sundays in a year and they buy the paper only on Sundays, what will they spend in 1 year?

   a. $39.00

   b.   9.00

   c.   28.00

3. The Andersons can save 15% of the monthly rate by ordering and paying on an annual basis. What is the annual rate?

   a. $100.00

   b.   81.60

   c.   75.00

4. What do the Andersons save if they drop the monthly rate and pay the annual rate?

   a. $10.00

   b.   14.40

   c.   24.00

5. If the Andersons subscribe for 1 year and cancel their subscription 6 months later, what will be their refund?

   a. $61.20

   b.   40.80

   c.   72.00

Consumer Education and Independent Living

Name _____ Date _____ Period _____ Score _____

Objective: Compute percentages; write a paragraph leading to a conclusion. **(Math, Writing)**

SPENDING YOUR BIRTHDAY MONEY

Directions: You have just celebrated your birthday. Although you did
not receive many gifts, you found that many of the cards contained
money, including $50 from your family. The total was $125.00. You
want to buy one nice gift. After shopping at the stores near you, and
determining what you need to add to your wardrobe, you have decided
to buy a suit. Fortunately, suits are on sale right now and you can go ahead
and buy! Remember that sales tax (say, 7%) must be included in the $125.00.

1. Which suit can you afford to buy? (Check one)

   SUIT A _____   SUIT B _____   SUIT C _____

2. Calculate the sales tax and total cost and write your answers in the spaces
   provided.

SUITS	ORIGINAL PRICE	SALE PRICE	7% SALES TAX	TOTAL COST
A	$139.00	$123.95	$_____	$_____
B	$125.00	$116.49	$_____	$_____
C	$129.95	$119.95	$_____	$_____

3. Which suit is reduced the most in price?

   SUIT A _____   SUIT B _____   SUIT C _____

4. Calculate the *percent* of reduction on each of the three suits.
   (Round off to the nearest percent)

   SUIT A _____   SUIT B _____   SUIT C _____

5. Write a paragraph explaining what other factors should be considered
   when purchasing expensive garments, other than price alone.

   _____

   _____

   _____

   _____

   _____

   _____

Consumer Education and Independent Living

Objective: Find percentages and fractions of amounts. **(Math)**

SPENDING MONEY BY PERCENTAGES AND FRACTIONS

Different people prefer to spend their money in different ways. Sometimes they spend because of need, while at other times their money is spent on things they want.

These students have set aside various percentages or fractions of their allowances and income for various needs and wants.

Directions: Please calculate how many *dollars* they will spend on the items listed below.

1. Sherrie has a weekly allowance of $8.00. She spends 35% of her money on food, 25% of her allowance on clothing, and 10% of her money on savings. How much does Sherrie spend per week for:

   Food $_____
   Clothing $_____
   Savings $_____
   Left for other needs and wants $_____
   TOTAL $_____

2. José earns $40.00 each week and receives $5.00 a week as an allowance. He uses 1/2 of his money for food and school supplies, 1/4 of his money on clothes, and saves 1/20 of his money. How much does José spend per week for:

   Food/School Supplies $_____
   Clothes $_____
   Savings $_____
   Left for other needs and wants $_____
   TOTAL $_____

3. Denise has an allowance of $10.50 each week and earns $6.00 a week baby-sitting. She is saving to buy a new jacket, which costs $50.00. She spends 20% of her money on food, spends 10% of it on records and entertainment, saves 20% for her new jacket, spends another 25% on cosmetics and jewelry, and saves the rest for a trip next summer. How much does Denise spend per week for:

   Food $_____
   Records, etc. $_____
   Savings for jacket $_____
   Cosmetics, etc. $_____
   Savings for trip $_____
   TOTAL $_____

4. David earns $12.00 a week mowing lawns and has a weekly allowance of $8.00. He spends 1/5 of his money on bus fare to and from school, 1/4 of his money on entertainment, 1/10 of his money on food, and saves the rest. How much does David spend per week for:

   Bus fare $_____
   Entertainment $_____
   Food $_____
   Savings $_____
   TOTAL $_____

Consumer Education and Independent Living

Name _____ Date _____ Period _____ Score _____

Objective: Find the percent of a number. **(Math)**

INTERESTED IN INTEREST?

Borrowing money or buying on credit costs money. *Interest* is the cost of borrowing money. It is the price you pay for buying now and paying later.

How Much Does Interest Cost?

The cost of interest is figured in *percent.* The symbol for percent is %. You probably are already familiar with percent. Should you answer correctly all the questions on a test, your teacher might say that you received 100%. Remember that 100% is all of something. 1% is 1/100 of something.

Figuring % of money is easy. 1 cent is 1% of a dollar. So:

1% of $ 1.00 is 1¢
1% of $10.00 is 10¢
1% of $15.00 is 15¢

(Hint: move the decimal point two places to the left.)

Directions: Remembering that 1¢ is 1% of a dollar, complete these problems:

1. 1% of $ 3.00 is $_____   3. 1% of $ 25.00 is $_____

2. 1% of $ 50.00 is $_____   4. 1% of $100.00 is $_____

Wait! There Is More!

Credit usually costs much more than 1%. Here is how to figure larger percents.

You do two steps: First, figure the amount for 1%.
                    Second, multiply the amount for 1% by the number of percent you need.

Here is an example: Problem: What is 8% of $50.00?

                      Answer: 1% of $50.00 is   ___50¢___
                               8 × 50¢ is $4.00 (8% of $50.00)

5. *Try this one:*   Problem: What is 12% of $60.00?

                      Answer: 1% of $60.00 is $____.____

                               12 × _____ is $_____ (12% of $60.00)

6. *Now try these:*   6% of $60.00 is _____

                       15% of $30.00 is _____

                        3% of $15.00 is _____

Consumer Education and Independent Living

Objective: Compute simple interest. **(Math)**

COMPUTING SIMPLE INTEREST

Simple interest is one way to calculate the cost of borrowing money. It is calculated on a yearly basis; it is not compounded daily. To find monthly simple interest, divide by 12.

How to calculate simple interest: *Multiply the amount borrowed by the percent of interest.* (Change the percent to a decimal before computing.)

Study the examples below:

a. 1% of $2,050 = $20.50

$$\begin{array}{r} \$2,050.00 \\ \times .01 \\ \hline \$20.50\ 00 \end{array}$$

b. 9% of $875 = $78.75

$$\begin{array}{r} \$875.00 \\ \times .09 \\ \hline \$78.7500 \end{array}$$

c. 1½% of $1,000 = $15.00

$$\begin{array}{r} \$\ 1,000.00 \\ \times .015 \\ \hline 500000 \\ 1000000 \\ \hline \$15.00000 \end{array}$$

d. 12¾% of $3,500 = $446.25

$$\begin{array}{r} \$\ \ \ \ 3,500 \\ \times .1275 \\ \hline 17500 \\ 245000 \\ 700000 \\ 3500000 \\ \hline \$446.2500 \end{array}$$

Directions: Calculate the answers to the following problems. Attach your calculation sheet. (Be sure to show all steps of your calculations.)

1. 2% interest on $45.00 $_____

2. 6% interest on $700.00 $_____

3. If Janet bought a used car for $3,250, how much simple interest would she pay on a 1-year loan if the interest rate is 15%? $_____

4. How much interest will accumulate after 1 month on a $1,200 savings account which earns 6% simple interest? $_____

5. How much simple interest would a lender charge on a $2,000 loan if the current interest rate is 16¾%? $_____

6. Bill and Jo-Lynn want to buy bedroom furniture. They can either charge it at the department store or borrow the money from a relative. It is cheaper for them to borrow the money from a relative than to charge it at a store. Below, calculate how much simple interest they will pay on $750 at 12% interest. $_____

Consumer Education and Independent Living

Name _____   Date _____   Period _____   Score _____

Objective: Compute the cost of installment buying; write a paragraph of personal opinion. **(Math; Writing)**

THE COST OF CREDIT

Betty plans to buy a new radio. It will cost her $75.00 cash. She does not have enough cash to pay for it, but could easily manage monthly payments of $10 to $12. Betty investigated the costs of buying the radio on credit, using three possible plans.

Plan A: Revolving Charge Account

The department store charges 1½% per month on the unpaid balance. Betty would make a down payment of $10.00, leaving a balance of $65.00 to be paid in 7 monthly installments. If the interest would be *less* than 50¢, the minimum charged is 50¢.

Plan B: Installment Plan

Betty considered buying the radio at a local appliance store. They use the installment plan for all credit purchases. Betty would finance $65.00, after making a down payment of $10.00. Each of 6 monthly payments would be $11.50.

Plan C: Acme Finance Company

Betty also considered a finance company, from whom she would borrow the entire $75.00. However, their annual percentage rate (APR) of interest is 30%. They only loan money for a 1-year period of time; each monthly payment would be $8.15.

Total Costs of Credit

Directions: Calculate the totals paid and cost of credit.

PLAN	AMOUNT FINANCED	MONTHLY PAYMENT	# OF MONTHS	TOTAL REPAID	COST OF * CREDIT
A	$65.00	$10.00 + 1½% on unpaid bal.	7	$69.58	$_____
B	$65.00	$11.50	6	$_____	$_____
C	$75.00	$ 8.15	12	$_____	$_____

*To find the cost of credit, subtract the amount financed from the total paid.

How to Calculate Interest on an Unpaid Balance in a Revolving Charge Account

To aid you in learning the way interest is calculated, the following calculations will be useful.

$ 75.00 Price of radio
−10.00 Down payment
$ 65.00 Amount to be financed

$ 65.00
X .015   (interest rate—1½% on unpaid balance.)
32500
65000
$.97500 or 98¢ interest

Consumer Education and Independent Living

THE COST OF CREDIT (cont.)

Payments in Seven Installments

$ 65.00	
+ .98 interest	
$ 65.98	
−10.00 1st payment	
$ 55.98	
+ .84 interest	
$ 56.82	
−10.00 2nd payment	
$ 46.82	
+ .70 interest	
$ 47.52	
−10.00 3rd payment	
$ 37.52	
+ .56 interest	
$ 38.08	
−10.00 4th payment	
$ 28.08	

$ 28.08	
+ .50 minimum charge	
$ 28.58	
−10.00 5th payment	
$ 18.58	
+ .50 minimum charge	
$ 19.08	
−10.00 6th payment	
$ 9.08	
+ .50 minimum charge	
$ 9.58	
− 9.58 7th payment	
$ 00.00	

Total Interest Charges

$ .98
.84
.70
.56
.50
.50
.50
$ 4.58

Directions: Please answer the following questions, using the information from the chart.

1. Which plan would cost Betty the least?

   Plan A _____   Plan B _____   Plan C _____

2. In comparing Plan A to Plan B, how much will Betty save if she decides

   on the less expensive one? $_____

3. Betty compared Plan B to Plan C. How much will she save if she uses

   the less expensive of the two plans? $_____

4. Please list the advantages and disadvantages of each plan.

PLAN	ADVANTAGES	DISADVANTAGES
A		
B		
C		

5. Which plan do you think Betty should adopt?

   Plan A _____   Plan B _____   Plan C _____

   Why? _____

6. How do you feel about the use of credit for major purchases? _____

_____

Consumer Education and Independent Living

Name   Date   Period   Score

Objective: Use percents in simple applications. **(Math)**

BANK ACCOUNT

1. You have $500 in your bank account. You withdraw ⅕ of the money to use on a bicycle. How much money do you have left in the account?

   $_____

2. Last year you were paid 8% simple interest by the bank. You had $650 in your savings account. How much interest did you receive?

   $_____

3. Your mother gave you $150 for your birthday. If you put it in the bank, it will earn 7½% interest in a year. How much interest will that be?

   $_____

4. Your sister has $305 in the bank. If she takes $15 out for her school project and earns 7% interest on the rest, what will be the total amount she has in the bank at the end of 12 months?

   $_____

5. If your father takes ⅓ of his salary of $1,500 and puts it in the bank, how much will he have left?

   $_____

6. You are saving $5 per week for a $150 stereo. How many weeks will it take you to save this amount?

   $_____

Consumer Education and Independent Living

Name _____ Date _____ Period _____ Score _____

Objective: Compute sums and differences of several amounts of money. **(Math)**

CREDIT CARDS

You are working part-time in Jackson's Clothing Store. Jim Johnson
bought the following items.

one belt	$ 9.98
one pair of slacks	18.98
one shirt	15.00

Directions: Please fill out the bank credit card slip. Use 6% as the sales tax.

```
5055   555   555   550            555555      0555
```

JIM JOHNSON

50555555 55BA
Jackson's Clothing *25
Chicago, IL

AUTH. NO.	DATE MO.	DAY	YR		DEPT.	INITIALS	☐ TAKE ☐ SEND
QUAN.	CLASS	DESCRIPTION				UNIT COST	AMOUNT

The issuer of the card identified on this item is authorized to pay the amount shown as TOTAL upon proper presentation I promise to pay such TOTAL (together with any other charges due thereon) subject to and in accordance with the agreement governing the use of such card

SIGN HERE X

SALES SLIP

SUB TOTAL _____
TAX _____
TOTAL _____

Directions: Please circle the letter of the best answer to each question.

1. If Jim returns the slacks, the refund amount will be

   a. $20.12

   b. 18.98

   c. 17.84

2. With a refund for the slacks, the new cost of Jim's bill will be

   a. $23.96

   b. 46.60

   c. 26.48

Consumer Education and Independent Living

Name   Date   Period   Score

Objective: Compute area measurements. (Math)

ROOM FLOOR PLAN

Directions: Mrs. Jones is planning to buy carpeting for her living room. Study the room floor plan. Use the information to answer items 1–4 below. Circle the letter of the best answer to each question.

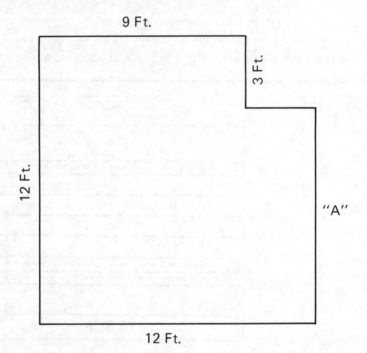

1. How long is the side of the room marked "A"?

   a. 3 ft.

   b. 6 ft.

   c. 9 ft.

   d. 12 ft.

2. How would you find the number of square feet in the room?

   a. Multiply 12 × 12

   b. Multiply 9 × 12 and add 9

   c. Multiply 12 × 12 and subtract 6

   d. Multiply 12 × 12 and subtract 9

3. There are 9 square feet in 1 square yard. How many square yards are in the room?

   a. 12

   b. 15

   c. 16

   d. 24

4. What is the distance around the room counting all 6 walls?

   a. 21 feet

   b. 42 feet

   c. 48 feet

   d. 54 feet

Consumer Education and Independent Living

Name _____ Date _____ Period _____ Score _____

Objective: Subtract numbers, regrouping if necessary. **(Math)**

READING A GRAPH

Directions: During the 30 years between 1950 and 1980, housing costs increased at a tremendous rate. Study the chart and circle the best answers to the questions.

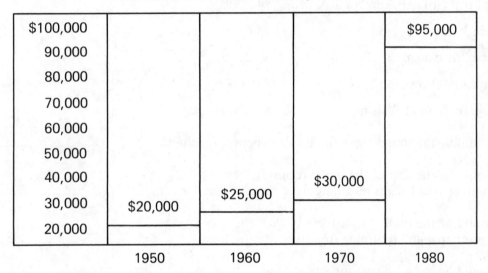

AVERAGE COST OF HOUSES, 1950–1980

1. What is the difference in the average cost of houses between 1950 and 1980?

   a. $70,000

   b. $75,000

   c. $57,000

2. When did the greatest increase occur?

   a. Between 1950–1960

   b. Between 1960–1970

   c. Between 1970–1980

3. If a family purchases a $100,000 home and makes a down payment of 20%, what balance will they have left to pay?

   a. $60,000

   b. $80,000

   c. $20,000

4. What is the percent of increase in the average cost of houses between 1950 and 1980?

   a. 475%

   b. 300%

   c. 175%

Consumer Education and Independent Living

Name   Date   Period   Score

Objectives: Multiply and divide amounts of money by a whole number; write a list of advantages and disadvantages. **(Math; Writing)**

PLANNING A HOLIDAY

Directions: Sue and Jane are planning a trip during their summer vacation. They must decide whether to fly or drive to their destination. Use the following information and help them make a decision.

Round-trip airline tickets for 2	$425.00
Mileage 1 way	1,000 miles
Automobile expenses	$0.21 mile
Average motel cost for 2	$35.00 per night
Average daily food costs for 2	$25.00 per day

1. What would be the round-trip automobile expenses for the trip? $_____

2. What would be the cost of the motel rooms if they spent 2 nights going and 1 night returning from their destination? $_____

3. What would be the total cost of their meals if they spent 3 days going to and 2 returning from their destination. $_____

4. What would be the total cost for Sue and Jane to drive to and from their destination? $_____

5. If they decided to divide all costs in half, how much would each person spend? $_____

6. What is the *difference* in cost between flying and driving round trip? Is it less expensive or more expensive to drive? $_____

7. List some of the advantages and disadvantages of driving, as opposed to flying.

_____

_____

_____

_____

_____

Consumer Education and Independent Living

Name _____ Date _____ Period _____ Score _____

Objective: Compute the sales tax. **(Math)**

BUYING SPORTS EQUIPMENT

Directions: Karri and John have seen the following advertisement for a skiing equipment sale. They both need to buy some items. Read the advertisement and answer the questions in the spaces provided.

ANDERSON'S SKIERS' SALE

	WERE	NOW			WERE	NOW
SKIS	$179.95	$129.00	GLOVES/MITTS from		$29.95	$19.00
BOOTS	89.95	49.00	SWEATERS from		89.95	49.00
JACKETS	95.95	58.00	GOGGLES from		20.95	14.00
PANTS	59.95	39.00	MASKS/HATS from		11.95	7.00

1. Karri bought a jacket, a pair of pants, and mitts. What is her total cost? $_____

2. What is the 6% tax on a sweater? $_____

3. John bought a sweater and a pair of skis. What is his total cost, including 6% sales tax? $_____

Other customers are finding Anderson's skiers' sale to be a source of good equipment at reasonable prices. Please answer the following questions in the spaces provided.

4. If someone purchased 1 pair of mitts, how much change would he or she receive from $25.00? (include 6% sales tax) $_____

5. Someone decided to buy 2 masks and 1 hat as gifts. What is the total cost, including 6% sales tax? How much change would be returned from a $50.00 bill? $_____

6. Another person purchased a sweater, a pair of goggles, and a mask. How much change should be returned from two $50.00 bills? (Include 6% sales tax.) $_____

Consumer Education and Independent Living

Name _____   Date _____   Period _____   Score _____

Objective: Use mathematics to organize an approach to problem-solving. **(Math)**

THE HIGH COST OF SHOPLIFTING

Shoplifting costs consumers a great deal of money. If something is shoplifted, its cost is passed on to the consumer in the form of higher prices on all items.

Directions: You are the owner of a small department store. You find that the following items have been stolen from your store. (The unit prices are in parentheses.)

1 sweater ($20.00)	5 greeting cards (80¢)
2 necklaces ($5.00)	1 picture frame ($6.00)
8 small cosmetics ($2.50)	3 boxes stationery ($2.00)
2 scarves ($4.00)	7 skeins yarn ($1.50)

You now need to determine how much you will raise prices to cover the thefts. (Show your calculations on a separate paper.)

1. What is your total dollar loss? $_____

2. To recover the $20 lost on one sweater, how many sweaters will need to be priced at $21?   _____

3. The price of the $5 necklaces will have to be raised to $6.00. How many will need to be sold at the new price to recover the original loss?   _____

4. What will the new price have to be on 40 cosmetics to recover the amount lost on the 8 that were stolen? $_____

5. The scarves, greeting cards, and picture frame losses totaled how many dollars? $_____

6. If the price of each item increased 25¢, how many items would need to be sold at the new price to recover the losses of the scarves, greeting cards, and picture frames?   _____

7. If the store decided to hire a part-time, plain-clothes security officer whose annual salary would be $12,000, how much would they need to raise the price on 5,000 items, with an average price of $12.00, to cover his or her salary? $_____

8. If he or she would recover or prevent the theft of $15,000 of merchandise per year, how much would be saved by the store if he or she were hired? $_____

9. Who eventually pays for shoplifting? _____

10. What can ultimately happen to a store where shoplifting is a major problem?

_____

_____

CAREERS

Teacher-Managed Reading Activities

BUILDING VOCABULARY

1. Prefix Activity

Use the career vocabulary list and have the students underline all the prefixes of the words. Have them classify the prefixes as:

- Negative prefixes
- Directional prefixes
- Quantitative prefixes
- Conditional prefixes
- Time prefixes

2. Suffix Activity

Use the career vocabulary list and have the students circle all the suffixes and classify them as:

- Noun suffixes
- Verb suffixes
- Adjective suffixes
- Adverb suffixes

3. Ten Career Words a Week

Select about ten words per week which relate to careers.

- Print the words on a large poster, large enough so they can be seen across a classroom. Students practice spelling as well as looking up definitions.
- Prepare a master for each week, with spaces for synonyms and/or antonyms as well as definitions.

IMPROVING COMPREHENSION

1. Ad Search

Have the students read Help Wanted ads and answer the following questions regarding specific jobs:

- Who is eligible to apply?
- What qualifications are necessary for the job?
- When are applications being accepted?
- Where is the place of employment?
- Why would you be qualified for the job?
- How much is the starting pay?

(*Literal Comprehension*)

2. Career Information

Have the students classify career information into similar groups
or categories:

- Under one heading: Part-Time Jobs, Careers, People-Oriented Jobs
- Under one time frame: Jobs Expecting Employment Opportunities
- Under one place frame: Jobs Located Outdoors, Desk Jobs

(*Literal Comprehension*)

3. Reaction to Careers

Have the students read information about various careers and react
personally to the information. Why or why not would they like the
job? (*Inferential Comprehension*)

4. Analyzing Statements

Have the students read statistics about various professions and
analyze the fallacies of reasoning, if any, in the statistics.

Example: Graduates of Harvard University earn an average
                   salary of $50,000 a year.
                   (The questions that need to be raised are: How was
                   the information obtained? What type of average was
                   used—mean, median, or mode? Is income a factor of
                   education or inheritance, etc?)

(*Analytical Comprehension*)

LOCATION-STUDY SKILLS

Plan exercises to give students practice in locating information in or
on:

- W-2 form wage and tax statement
- Yellow pages of the telephone directory
- Periodicals
- Dictionary of Occupational Titles
- Counseling center
- Library
- City hall

CAREERS

Teacher-Managed Writing Activities

WRITING LISTS

(Refer to Appendix 13.)

1. List the steps in preparing a one-page résumé.
2. List the steps in preparing a one-page application.

JOURNAL WRITING

(Refer to Appendix 1.)

Use the following open-ended sentences to give the students the opportunity to practice their writing skills as they gain insight into their own thoughts and feelings.

- As I face the future I . . .
- The thought of working . . .
- It will be difficult to . . .
- I plan to . . .
- I love to . . .
- When something doesn't work out I . . .

FILMSTRIP WRITING

(Refer to Appendixes 2–4.)

Begin with prewriting activities and be sure that editing and rewriting occurs, before the drawing begins. Suggested topics include:

- Ways to handle an interview
- Dress for success ideas
- Speaking with confidence

LETTER TO THE EDITOR

(Refer to Appendix 5.)

It is a thrill to see in print one's own letter to an editor! The students could have this opportunity if they would write a relevant, up-to-date letter. Suggested topics include:

- Employment opportunities for youth
- Summertime employment

CONSUMER BUSINESS LETTER

(Refer to Appendix 6.)

1. Write a letter of application to a college.
2. Write a letter requesting an interview for a job that was advertised in the newspaper.

DRAWING MAPS/READING AND FOLLOWING MAPS

(Refer to Appendixes 11–12.)

Give the students practice in writing directions to get from one location to another and learning how to draw a map to show a particular location:

1. Write the directions for going to a destination on campus, starting in your present classroom.
2. Draw a map for going to the same destination, starting in your present classroom.
3. Write the directions and draw a map of how to go from your school to your home.
4. Draw a map (use a city map if you travel by bus any great distance) for returning home from school.

CAREERS

Vocabulary List

abbreviation
ability
accomplishment
achievement
adjustment
administration
advancement
advertise
agency
aggressive
agreement
ambition
analyze
appearance
applicant
application
appointment
apprentice
appropriate
aptitude
apitude test
arrested
artistic
assertive
asset
assignment
attendance
attentive
attitude
authorize
available
aware

base pay
behavior
benefits
business

capabilities
capable
career
career planning
categorize
character
check
civil service
classification
classified ad
clerical

clusters
college
commission
compensation
conditions
confidence
confidential
consideration
consultant
contact
contract
contribution
convenience
convey
convict
cooperative
counseling
counselor
courtesy
co-worker
creative
credit bureau

decision
deduction
degree
dependent
description
detail
determination
develop
directory
disability
disability insurance
disclose
discriminate
dismissal
documents
duties

economy
education
effective
efficient
employee
employer
employment
employment agency
employment history

energy
enterprise
enthusiasm
environment
equal opportunity
    employer
evaluation
examination
exemption
experience
extra-curricular

fee
feelings
felony
form
former
free lance
fringe benefits
full-time
function
future

garnish
goals
grooming
gross pay
group insurance
guarantee
guidance
guide

health insurance
high school
hobby
honesty
hours

identification
identify
imagination
impression
income
income tax
independence
independent
index
individual
industry

influence
information
informative
initiate
initiative
instructions
insurance
intelligence test
interests
interview
inventory
investigate
investigation
itemized deduction

job
job description
job hunt
job market
job search
job sharing
job source
job title
judgment
junior college

knowledge

labor
labor union
leader
legal
leisure
license
life insurance
likes
locate
location
loyalty

manage
management
manager
manual
manual dexterity
manual labor
marital status
maximum
measure
membership
mental

minimum requirements
minimum wage
motivation

needs
negotiate
net pay
newspaper
numerical ability

obligation
observe
obstacles
occupation
offer
opportunity
origin
original
organization
organize

part-time
pay
paycheck
payroll
pension
percentage
performance
permanent
persistence
personal
personal data sheet
personality
personnel
personnel office
persuasive
physical skills
placement
placement office
planning
policy
position
potential
praise
preference
preparation
principles
priorities
private
privilege
processing

profession
professional
progress
prohibited
promotion
prompt
punctuation
purpose

qualifications
qualities

rate
rating scale
realistic
realize
recommendation
records
recruiter
reference
register
relationship
release
reliable
reputation
requirement
residence
resources
responsibilities
résumé
retirement

salary
sample
satisfaction
schedule
school
secure
security
self-confidence
self-employment
self-esteem
self-evaluation
self-image
self-worth
senses
sick leave
signature
skills
social security
source

specialize
specific
split shift
spouse
standard
stock plan
succeed
success
suggested
summary
survey

talent
task
taxable income
taxes
tax return
technical
technical school
temporary
trade school
train
transferable skills

union

valid
values
verify
veteran
violation
vocation
vocational education
volunteer

wage
want ads
wants
withholding
work
worker's compensation
work experience
work load
work permit

yellow pages

CAREERS

Student Worksheets—Teaching Strategies

The answers for the Careers student worksheets are found in the Answer Key, p. 227. Teaching strategies for selected student worksheets are found below.

EMPLOYMENT APPLICATION FORM

The students have a better chance of obtaining employment if they fill out the application form neatly, correctly, and completely. If they have interviews, their looks, manners, and ability to answer questions are extremely important.

CAREER INFORMATION OUTLINE

Information on careers is available in many places. Career centers and libraries are good places to begin research. Three titles are recommended here:

Dictionary of Occupational Titles (DOT). Describes about 20,000 jobs according to duties of workers. Includes list of tools and/or equipment used, if appropriate. The nine *categories* of occupations listed in the DOT are: Professional, Technical and Managerial; Clerical and Sales; Service; Agriculture; Fishing, Forestry and Related; Processing; Machine Trades; Bench Work; Structural Work; Miscellaneous. (Printed by Superintendent of Documents, Government Printing Office, Washington, DC 20402.)

The Occupational Outlook Handbook (OOH). Describes such things as the nature of the work, places of employment, outlook, earnings, and related occupations. The thirteen *occupational clusters* covered in the OOH are: Industrial Procedures; Office; Service; Education; Sales; Construction; Transportation; Scientific and Technical; Mechanics and Repairers; Health; Social Science; Social Service; Performing Arts, Design and Communication. (Printed by Superintendent of Documents, Government Printing Office, Washington, DC 20402.)

Career Information Center (CIC), 13 volumes. Uses the same categories as the above volumes, but they are titled and divided into volumes differently, e.g., administration, business and office (1); agribusiness, environment, and natural resources (2); communications and the arts (3); construction (4); consumer, homemaking and personal services (5); engineering, science and technology (6); health (7); hospitality and recreation (8); manufacturing (9); marketing and distribution (10); public and community services (11); transportation (12); master index (13). (Printed by Glencoe Publishing Company, 17337 Ventura Blvd., Encino, CA 91316.)

THE DELI

Students need practice in calculating cost per unit or item, which this exercise provides. In addition, students need to know that the prices in restaurants are not only for food; the receipts must cover overhead, salaries, profit, etc. Businesses cannot stay in business unless all costs are covered. This exercise provides students with the opportunity to calculate some of these costs.

Careers

Name _____ Date _____ Period _____ Score _____

Objective: Recognition and utilization of abbreviations in everyday situations. **(Reading)**

ABBR. = ABBREVIATIONS

Directions: Classified ads often use abbreviations to save space and money in advertising available work.

1. Attach four classified ads in the space below.
2. Underline two or more abbreviations in each ad.
3. List the abbreviation next to the ad.
4. Write out the word abbreviated next to the abbreviation.
   Example: resp. = responsibility

Attach Ads Below

Careers

Name   Date   Period   Score

Objective: Identify relevant/irrelevant information. **(Reading)**

CLASSIFIED ADS: HELP WANTED

CHEF

Experienced working chef required for busy hotel. Heavy banquet experience essential. Apply in person to the Food and Beverage Director, Holiday Inn, 21333 Hawthorne Blvd., Skokie, IL 60077

FIRST COOK

For Maine summer resort. Must be able to work with dinner house menu, mostly fish and seafood. Housing provided: June–Oct. Confidential, call Ted (818) 555-5555.

COOK–TRAINEE

El Encanto Hotel of Miami is offering cook–trainee positions to young, energetic people who wish to study nouvelle cuisine. Experience not necessary. Contact chef, 1900 Lasuen Road. (305) 555-5555

Directions: Read the ads and answer the following questions.

1. a. What type of experience is necessary for the chef position?

   _____

   _____

   b. To whom should you apply for this position?

   _____

   c. Can you telephone to apply?

   _____ yes _____ no

2. a. Where is the first cook position available?

   _____

   b. Is this a year-round job?

   _____ yes _____ no

   Explain _____

   _____

   _____

3. a. In what city is the cook–trainee position available?

   _____

   b. What should the trainee be willing to study?

   _____

   c. What does nouvelle cuisine mean?

   _____

   _____

   d. Is experience necessary?

   _____ yes _____ no

   e. Who should be contacted about this job?

   _____

Careers

Objective: Use dictionary entry word information to find definitions and synonyms. **(Reading)**

READ BEFORE YOU SIGN (I)

"I certify that the answers given by me to the foregoing questions and statements are true and correct without consequential omissions of any kind whatsoever. I agree that the company shall not be liable in any respect if my employment is terminated because of the falsity of statements, answers, or omissions made by me in this questionnaire. I also authorize the companies, schools, or persons named above to give any information regarding my employment, together with any information they may have regarding me whether or not it is in their records. I hereby release said companies, schools, or persons from all liability for any damage for issuing this information."

This statement is an example of one you may have to sign in agreement when you complete an application form. Read it carefully and then follow the directions below.

Directions: Use a dictionary to find a synonym(*) and definition for each of the words below.

Word	Synonym	Definition
1. certify		
2. foregoing		
3. consequence		
4. omission		
5. liable		
6. terminate		
7. questionnaire		
8. false		
9. authorize		
10. liability		

*Synonym: A word which means the same as another word, e.g., **big** and **large**.

Careers

Objective: Develop paragraphs by different methods (examples, definitions). **(Writing)**

READ BEFORE YOU SIGN (II)

Rewrite the agreement from the first page in your own words. Write it as you would explain it to someone who does not understand the meaning of the guarantee. You may use your own words as well as some of the synonyms(*).

_____

_____

_____

_____

_____

_____

_____

_____

_____

_____

_____

_____

_____

_____

_____

_____

_____

_____

*Synonym: A word which means the same as another word, e.g., **big** and **large.**

Careers

Objectives: Compile a résumé; write a letter to the editor; write a letter of request. **(Writing)**

PREWRITING EXPERIENCES FOR CAREERS

I. Classroom Activities

To help you write successful résumés and cover letters, the following classroom activities might be helpful.

1. Invite a neighborhood business person to speak to the class about what he or she looks for when reading résumés and cover letters.

2. Role-play the parts of employers at various places of employment. (If students were employers, what would they look for in employees?)

3. Participate in a class discussion centering around the following topics:

- what you would like to do
- where to find such a job
- what information is needed in applying for the job
- do you have the right qualifications
- keeping track of your job assets, work history, education, etc.
- knowing the benefits the company will receive because of your employment
- experience gained with job(s) that will be useful in the future
- resources—who will help you in locating a job, writing a recommendation, etc.
- submitting the right kind of résumé and cover letter for the job in question
- the way your letter and résumé look

II. Assignments

1. Write a cover letter and résumé for a particular job, using want ads as the basis for writing.

2. Write a letter to the editor of a local newspaper about job opportunities for young people in the community, or on training available for non-traditional jobs.

3. Write business letters to various companies, asking them about both necessary qualifications for various jobs, as well as job benefits.

Careers

Objective: Complete a job application form. **(Writing)**

EMPLOYMENT APPLICATION FORM

Direction: Fill out the sample employment form below.

JOB	1. Job Applying for				2. Code Number	

PERSONAL DATA

3. Name: Last	First	Middle	4. Social Security Number
5. Present Address: Number and Street	City	State	Zip Code

6. Birthdate: Month	Day	Year	7. Home Phone	8. Work Phone	9. Fluent in What Other Languages

EDUCATION

10. Circle Highest Grade Completed 6 7 8 9 10 11 12	Date Completed	Did you Graduate? ☐ Yes ☐ No	If Not, Have You Passed a GED Test? ☐ Yes ☐ No

11. Name and Location of Colleges or Trade Schools Attended	Date Attended	Units Completed Sem. Qtr.		Major Subject or Course	Degree or Cert.
	From				
	To				
	From				
	To				
	From				
	To				

WORK EXPERIENCE (Paid and Unpaid)

12. Begin with your most recent job. List all jobs (include part-time work) you have held in the last 10 years.

From / To	Name of Employer	Your Title
Total Months	Address	Duties:
Hours per week	City and State	
Monthly Salary	Supervisor's Name	Reason for Leaving:

From / To	Name of Employer	Your Title
Total Months	Address	Duties:
Hours per week	City and State	
Monthly Salary	Supervisor's Name	Reason for Leaving:

From / To	Name of Employer	Your Title
Total Months	Address	Duties:
Hours per week	City and State	
Monthy Salary	Supervisor's Name	Reason for Leaving:

From / To	Name of Employer	Your Title
Total Months	Address	Duties:
Hours per week	City and State	
Monthly Salary	Supervisor's Name	Reason for Leaving:

Careers

Objective: Compile a résumé. **(Writing)**

RÉSUMÉS

Directions: A personal résumé should provide a complete picture of your qualifications in a format that is easy to read. On a separate piece of paper, write your own personal résumé based on the following example. Write only the facts about yourself.

Sample Résumé

PERSONAL DATA	Jane A. Smith 360 North Street Los Angeles, CA 90052 (Telephone: 818-628-3984)
POSITION APPLYING FOR	Stenographer
EDUCATION	Graduate, 1980, of Walnut High School, Los Angeles

EDUCATION

Major Subjects: Typing (1 year, "A" grade, 70 words per minute)
Shorthand (2 years, "A–" average, 120 words per minute)
Business English and Communication (1 semester, "B" grade)
Bookkeeping (1 year, "A" grade)

Extracurricular: Secretary of junior class
Reporter for school newspaper

Honors: Service Award for Outstanding Business Student, 1979–80

EXPERIENCE

July, 1978 to September, 1978

and

July, 1979 to September, 1979

Sanford's Department Store, Los Angeles, as a clerk-stenographer

Duties: Preparing and mailing invoices, taking dictation, transcribing, typing correspondence, taking inventory of supplies, ordering supplies, filing and duplicating

Salary: $120 to $150 per week

REFERENCES (with permission)

Mrs. Evelyn Brown, Office Manager
Sanford's Department Store
9842 Yosemite Street
Los Angeles, California 90050
(Telephone: 213-638-4902)

Mr. Eugene Davis, Principal
Walnut High School
1408 N. Skyline Avenue
Los Angeles, California 90052
(Telephone: 213-634-1082)

Miss Jane Hamilton, Instructor, Business Education
Walnut High School
1408 N. Skyline Avenue
Los Angeles, California 90052
(Telephone: 213-634-1082)

Careers

Objective: Write a letter of application for a job. **(Writing)**

LETTER OF APPLICATION FOR EMPLOYMENT (I)

The Content of a Letter

The content of a letter can be compared to what might be said in a personal business call. The usual sequence of a call is as follows:

- Greetings
- Statement of the business of the call
- Concluding remarks

The average business letter will follow the same plan, in that it will include:

- An opening statement
- Paragraph or paragraphs containing the message
- Conclusion or summary

The body of a letter should be clear, complete, concise, and courteous. You must understand exactly what you want to say. Then you must word the message in an orderly manner. Include essential details and cover the entire subject in the fewest possible words. A letter should be concise, but not be so brief as to be discourteous.

The Letter of Application

In composing the body of a letter of application for employment, you should consider the following suggestions:

- The first twenty-five words are important. They should be planned to attract the reader's attention at once.
- Tell your story in terms of the contribution you can make to the firm and to the employer.
- Be sure your letter and résumé are tailored to the job for which you are applying.
- Be sure you refer to your résumé. It gives the facts.
- With local firms, take the initiative in suggesting that you telephone for an interview.
- Use simple, direct language and correct grammar. Avoid worn out expressions.
- Type neatly on clean bond paper (white).
- Keep the letter short. You need not repeat the information that is in your résumé.
- Your letter should sum up what you have to offer and act as an "introduction card" for your résumé.
- Let your letter reflect your individuality, but avoid sounding aggressive, overbearing, familiar, cute, or humorous. Remember that you are writing to a stranger about a subject that is serious to both of you.

Careers

Objective: Write a letter of application for a job. **(Writing)**

LETTER OF APPLICATION FOR EMPLOYMENT (II)

Directions: On a separate piece of paper, compose a letter of application for employment to accompany your résumé. Use the same letter below as a guide.

360 North Street
Los Angeles, CA 90052
October 16, 1981

Mr. George R. Simpson
Personnel Director
ABC Manufacturing Company
800 Orange Avenue
Los Angeles, CA 90632

Dear Mr. Simpson:

Mr. Jones, career advisor at Walnut High School, has informed me that there is an opening in your organization for a competent stenographer. I would appreciate your considering my application for this position, as I feel I have the right qualifications.

You will note from the enclosed résumé that I have had extensive training in business courses and have achieved a high standard of speed in both typewriting and shorthand. Although I have been employed only during school vacation periods, I have a genuine liking for office work. If given an opportunity, I will work hard to prove that I am an asset to your company.

May I ask that you read my résumé and permit me to telephone your secretary next week to arrange for an appointment?

Sincerely yours,

Jane A. Smith

Enclosure: Résumé

Careers

Objective: Write paragraphs describing qualifications for a job. **(Writing)**

THE JOB INTERVIEW

Directions: A job interview is a very important step in the process of getting a job. You are presenting yourself to the employer, and at the same time, you have an opportunity to learn about the job. To help you prepare for your first, second, or third interview, please answer the following question. Use complete sentences and correct spelling and punctuation.

Question: If *you* were an employer, what qualifications would you look for in an employee for the job listed below?

TYPE OF BUSINESS _____ (e.g., fast food, manufacturing, hospital work, etc.)

TYPE OF JOB AT THIS BUSINESS _____ (e.g., fry cook, seamstress, nurses' helper, etc.)

EMPLOYEE QUALIFICATIONS _____

_____

_____

_____

_____

_____

_____

_____

_____

_____

_____

_____

_____

_____

_____

_____

Careers

Name   Date   Period   Score

Objective: Write a report, developing opinions or values supported by specific facts. **(Writing)**

CAREER INFORMATION OUTLINE

Directions: Read a variety of materials on jobs which interest you. When you find *one* that is most intriguing, find out as much as you can about it. The questions below will help you organize your written report. Jot down some notes under each category and use them in your report.

1. What kind of work would you do? What would your duties be? What would the working conditions be?

   _____

   _____

2. If appropriate, what kind of tools and/or equipment would you use?

   _____

3. What skills and/or abilities do you need for this kind of work?

   _____

4. How do you know if you would like or could learn this kind of work?

   _____

5. How can you prepare for and enter this kind of work? What kind of training and/or education would you need? Would your employer pay any or all of it?

   _____

   _____

6. What else should you consider about this job? What are the opportunities for advancement? What are the benefits, including such things as insurance, a feeling of contributing, etc?

   _____

   _____

7. What could you expect to earn at different levels?

   _____

8. What is the outlook for employment in your chosen field during the following years?

   _____

9. What are some of the related occupations and/or job titles?

   _____

10. Where can you find more information about the job?

    _____

11. Name any miscellaneous requirements, such as union membership, etc.

    _____

    _____

Careers

Name   Date   Period   Score

Objective: Compute the distance a car travels. **(Math)**

FIGURING MILEAGE

Directions: John has a new job and is trying to decide the shortest distance from home to work. Study the chart and answer the questions below. Circle the letter of the best answer to each question.

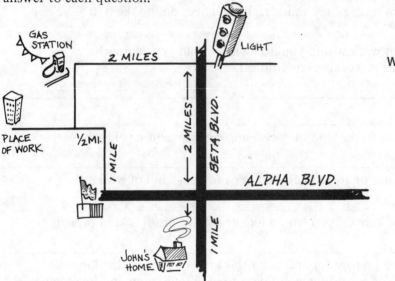

1. How many miles will John travel if he leaves home and travels north on Beta, then turns west at the light, south at the gas station, and west to work?

   a. 5 miles

   b. 7 miles

   c. 6 miles

2. How many miles will he travel if he leaves home, turns west on Alpha at Beta, and takes that route to work?

   a. 5 miles

   b. 4 miles

   c. 6 miles

3. What is the savings in mileage driven per day, round trip, between the longer and shorter route?

   a. 6 miles

   b. 4 miles

   c. 2 miles

4. If he drives the shorter route, how many miles will he drive per 5-day work week, round trip?

   a. 25 miles

   b. 37 miles

   c. 50 miles

Careers

Name   Date   Period   Score

Objective: Compute the sales tax. **(Math)**

CALCULATING SALES TAX

Many states charge a sales tax on certain items to help pay for the expenses of running the state government. You work in a small store with a regular, non-computer cash register and are required to hand-write bills for items sold. You usually use a tax table to figure out the tax, but it has been misplaced. You are too busy writing up sales to look for it.

Directions: Calculate the amount of sales tax on the following items in your store. The sales tax is 8%.

ITEM	PRICE	DOLLAR AMOUNT OF 8% SALES TAX	TOTAL COST
Sweater	$ 15.95	$.	$.
Blouse	19.95	.	.
Polo shirt	11.95	.	.
Shoes	28.00	.	.
Vest	17.95	.	.
Coat	99.99	.	.
Jacket	49.95	.	.
3-piece suit	109.95	.	.
Jeans	32.95	.	.
Scarf	5.89	.	.
Pants	22.50	.	.

Careers

Name _____   Date _____ Period _____ Score _____

Objective: Compute the take-home pay. **(Math)**

TIME AND WAGE CONCEPTS

1. Jan works 40 hours per week and earns $5.35 an hour. The
following are her weekly deductions:

State Income Tax	$ 6.42
Federal Income Tax	$42.80
Social Security (F.I.C.A.)	$14.34

In addition, she saves $15.00 at the credit union. Complete her
Statement of Earnings below. *Net pay* is the amount left to spend
on her living expenses after the other items are deducted.

GROSS PAY	F.I.C.A.	FEDERAL WITHHOLDING	STATE WITHHOLDING	CREDIT UNION	NET PAY
$	$	$	$	$	$

2. Sam works as a bagger at a local supermarket. His hours vary
each day. He earns $3.35 an hour. He gets a one-half hour,
non-paid meal break each day, except Wednesday.

Monday	8:00 a.m.	–	4:30 p.m. _____ hours
Tuesday	9:30 a.m.	–	6:00 p.m. _____ hours
Wednesday	12:00 noon	–	6:00 p.m. _____ hours
Thursday	7:00 a.m.	–	3:30 p.m. _____ hours
Saturday	12:00 noon	–	10:00 p.m. _____ hours

Calculate his gross pay and then complete his Statement of
Earnings. His deductions are:

State Income Tax	$ 4.02
Federal Income Tax	$26.80
Social Security (F.I.C.A.)	$ 8.98

GROSS PAY	F.I.C.A.	FEDERAL WITHHOLDING	STATE WITHHOLDING	CREDIT UNION	NET PAY
$	$	$	$	$	$

Careers

Name   Date   Period   Score

Objective: Compute the take-home pay. **(Math)**

CALCULATING WAGE DEDUCTIONS

Jerry is working at his first job in a shoe store. When he received his first paycheck, he was very surprised to find that he did not receive what he calculated he had earned. His boss told him about deductions and why *net pay* is quite different from *gross pay*.

Directions: Please calculate the following problems.

Regular Hours: 40 hours $3.80/hour $_____

Overtime Pay: 3 hours $5.70/hour $_____

                              GROSS PAY $_____

Percentages Withheld From Paychecks:

State Withholding Tax   3%
Federal Withholding Tax   20%
Social Security (F.I.C.A.)   6.7%
State Disability Tax   0.8%

Calculate each deduction in dollars, based on gross pay

a. State Withholding Tax $_____

b. Federal Withholding Tax $_____

c. Social Security (F.I.C.A.) $_____

d. State Disability $_____

                               Subtotal $_____

e. Jerry wants to put $10.00 in the credit union. $____10.00____

                                  Total $_____

Figure Jerry's Net Pay

                           Gross Pay $_____

                         Deductions $_____

                             Net Pay $_____

Careers

Objective: Compute the hourly pay and annual pay. **(Math)**

COMPUTING YOUR WAGE

Directions: Tom was promoted to the position of manager of the Red Anchor Restaurant. His salary was $6.80 per hour and is now $8.75 per hour. In the following activities, compute the amount of pay he received before and after his promotion.

1. To convert hourly pay to *pay per day,* multiply the hourly pay by the number of hours per work day.

   $ 6.80 per hour
   X 8 hours per work day
   $___.___ per day, before raise

   $ 8.75 per hour
   X 8 hours per work day
   $___.___ per day, after raise

2. To convert hourly pay to *pay per week:*

   a. Multiply the hourly pay by the number of hours per week.

   $ 6.80 per hour
   X 40 hours per week
   $___.___ per week, before raise

   $ 8.75 per hour
   X 40 hours per week
   $___.___ per week, after raise

   Or b. Multiply the daily pay (see number 1) by the number of days per week.

   $_____ per day
   X 5 days per week
   $_____ per week, before raise

   $_____ per day
   X 5 days per week
   $_____ per week, after raise

3. To compute the *pay per year,* multiply the weekly pay by the number of weeks per year.

   $_____ per week
   X 52 weeks per year
   $_____ per year, before raise

   $_____ per week
   X 52 weeks per year
   $_____ per year, after raise

4. What is the *difference* in yearly pay between an hourly rate of $6.80 and $8.75? $_____

Directions: Compute the following hourly wages to weekly and annual pay. Attach your computations. (*Reminder:* 40 hours per week and 52 weeks per year.)

CAREER	HOURLY WAGE	WEEKLY WAGES	YEARLY WAGES
Cosmetologist	$5.35	$	$
Child Care Aide	$4.50	$	$
Cashier	$3.75	$	$
Pattern Cutter	$8.25	$	$

Extra Credit

1. John works 35 hours and his pay per hour is $4.20. Compute the pay per week.

   $_____ per week

2. Compute his yearly income based on 35 hour weeks at $4.20 per hour.

   $_____ per year

Careers

Objective: Compute all income and charges in business transactions to determine profit or loss. **(Math)**

COST OF DELI FAVORITES (I)

Problem: John and Ginny own a small deli-restaurant which does its best business at noon with many people who work nearby. Customers can either eat there or take out food. On the menu, their best sellers are:

- Ham and Swiss Cheese Sandwich on Rye $3.00
  with dill pickle
- Small Dinner Salad/Dressing   .65
- Ice Cream Milk Shake   .95

Directions: Use the chart to do a cost analysis of the three most popular foods.

1. Find the *total* cost of the 14 foods in column C.
2. Find the *unit cost* of each of the 14 foods. Write your answers in column D.
3. Find the cost of *one serving* of each of the 14 foods. Write your answers in column F.
4. Find the total cost of the amounts calculated in column F.

Cost Analysis of Deli Foods

A Item	B Quantity Purchased	C Wholesale Cost of "B"	D Unit Cost	E Am't Needed for 1 serving	F Cost for making *one* serving
Rye bread	1½ lb. 24 slices	$ .55	$ /slice	2 slices	$
Ham	5 lbs. (80 oz.)	9.99	/oz.	2 oz.	
Swiss cheese	3 lbs (48 oz.)	3.89	/oz.	2 oz.	
Mayonnaise	1 gal. (256 T.)	3.49	/T.	1 T.	
Mustard	1 lb.jar (32T.)	1.19	/T.	½ T.	
Dill Pickles	1 lb. jar (9 pickles)	.99	/each	1	
Lettuce	12 heads (case)	3.25	/head	⅛ head	
Tomatoes	24	3.85	/each	½ tomato	
Radishes	10 bunches	1.69	/bunch	⅛ bunch	
Cucumbers	12	2.99	/each	⅛ cucumber	
Salad dressing Ingredients	1 quart (32 oz.)	.89	/T.	3 T.	
Milk	gallon 16 C	1.59	/cup	½ cup	
Ice Cream	gallon 16 C	2.09	/cup	½ cup	
Chocolate sauce	12 oz.	.79	/oz.	1 oz.	
TOTALS		(*)$.			(**)$.

(*)Original cost for all the food.

(**)Cost to make one serving of each of the best sellers on the menu.

Careers

Name   Date   Period   Score

Objectives: Compute all income and charges in business transactions to determine profit or loss; write a paragraph of personal opinion. **(Math; Writing)**

COST OF DELI FAVORITES (II)

Directions: John and Ginny need to charge enough for their restaurant food to cover the food costs, rent, utilities, insurance, upkeep, supplies, salaries, etc. In addition, they must pay the sales tax to the state. Find out what profit they make from their best sellers. Make the following calculations and record your answers in the spaces provided.

1. WHOLESALE FOOD COSTS TO RESTAURANT

   $_____ Total (from column F)

   X 125 _____ Customers

   $_____ Total food cost for 125 customers

2. RETAIL FOOD PRICES TO CUSTOMERS

   $_____ Total price (sandwich, salad, milk shake)

   X 125 _____ Customers

   a. $_____ Subtotal/Receipts

   b. +_____ 6% Sales tax collected

   c. _____ Total receipts for 1 day

3. BUSINESS OVERHEAD COSTS

   $_____ Subtotal/receipts (from #2a)

   −_____ Wholesale food costs (from #1)

   a. $_____ Money available for overhead and salaries

   X .75 _____ (75%)

   b. $_____ Amount needed for overhead

4. SALARIES AND PROFIT FOR JOHN AND GINNY

   $_____ Money available (from #3a)

   −_____ Amount needed for overhead and profit (from #3b)

   $_____ Salaries and profit for John and Ginny

5. Do you think you would like to go into the restaurant business? Why or why not?

   _____

   _____

   _____

PART III

STUDENT MANAGED ACTIVITIES IN SCIENCE

Foods and Nutrition

Name _____ Date _____ Period _____ Score _____

Objectives: Study food additives; use appropriate reference materials. **(Science; Reading)**

FOOD ADDITIVES (I)

Directions: In the library, find a dictionary of food additives. Look up each additive. List its major use in food. Then rate it NT (nontoxic), S (safe in small amounts), or F (further study is needed).

ADDITIVE	MAJOR USE IN FOOD	RATING
1. Aluminum calcium silicate		
2. Ammonium chloride		
3. Annatto		
4. Aspartame (Nutra-Sweet)		
5. Calcium disodium (EDTA)		
6. Calcium propionate		
7. Carotene		
8. Guar gum		
9. Lactic acid		
10. Mannitol		

Foods and Nutrition

Name   Date   Period   Score

Objectives: Study food additives; use appropriate reference materials. **(Science; Reading)**

FOOD ADDITIVES (II)

Directions: In the library, find a dictionary of food additives. Look up each additive. List its major use in food. Then rate it NT (nontoxic), S (safe in small amounts), or F (further study is needed).

ADDITIVE	MAJOR USE IN FOOD	RATING
1. Monosodium glutamate		
2. Nitrates		
3. Nitrites		
4. Polysorbate 80		
5. Propylene glycol		
6. Potassium chloride		
7. Saccharin		
8. Sodium benzoate		
9. Sodium bisulfite		
10. Sorbitol		

Foods and Nutrition

Name   Date   Period   Score

Objectives: Learn the importance and sources of vitamins; use appropriate reference materials. **(Science; Reading)**

THE IMPORTANCE OF VITAMINS

Directions: In the library, find a book about nutrition. Look up each vitamin. In the first column, write one or two important things that the vitamin does. In the second column, write one or two main food sources for that vitamin.

VITAMIN	IMPORTANCE	SOURCE
1. Vitamin A		
2. Vitamin B_1		
3. Vitamin B_2		
4. Vitamin B_6		
5. Vitamin B_{12}		
6. Vitamin B_{13}		
7. Biotin		
8. Vitamin C		
9. Vitamin D		
10. Vitamin E		
11. Niacin		
12. Folic Acid		
13. Pantothenic Acid		

Foods and Nutrition

Name _____ Date _____ Period _____ Score _____

Objectives: Learn the importance and sources of minerals; use appropriate reference materials. **(Science; Reading)**

THE IMPORTANCE OF MINERALS

Directions: In the library, find a book about nutrition. Look up each mineral. In the first column, write one or two important things about what the mineral does. In the second column, write one or two main food sources for that mineral.

MINERAL	IMPORTANCE	SOURCE
1. Calcium		
2. Phosphorus		
3. Iodine		
4. Iron		
5. Magnesium		
6. Manganese		
7. Zinc		
8. Potassium		

Parenting and Family Relationships

Name _____ Date _____ Period _____ Score _____

Objectives: Read a thermometer; interpret a drawing. **(Science; Reading)**

READING A THERMOMETER

Directions: Do some reading in the library about temperatures and what they mean. Read each thermometer. On the TEMPERATURE line, write the temperature. On the COMMENTS line, tell what the temperature means and what the person taking the temperature should do. The first problem is done for you as an example.

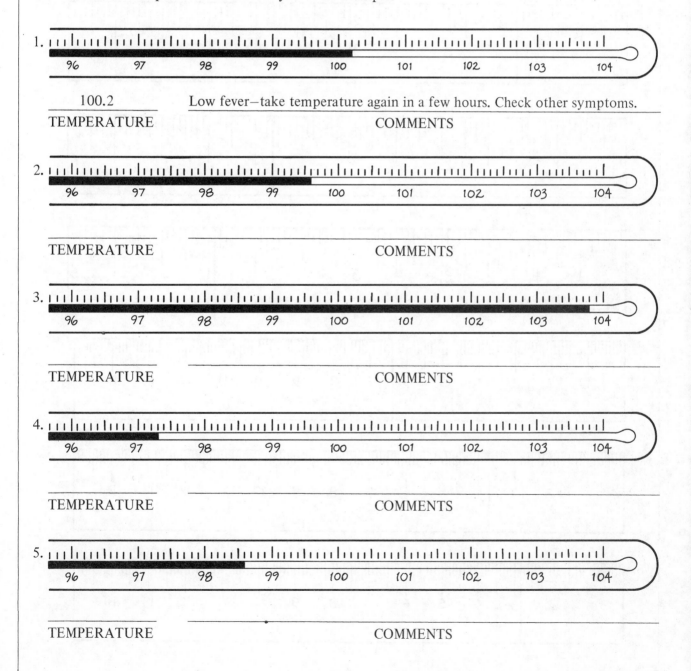

1.

| 100.2 | Low fever—take temperature again in a few hours. Check other symptoms. |
| TEMPERATURE | COMMENTS |

2.

TEMPERATURE _____ COMMENTS _____

3.

TEMPERATURE _____ COMMENTS _____

4.

TEMPERATURE _____ COMMENTS _____

5.

TEMPERATURE _____ COMMENTS _____

Clothing and Textiles

Name   Date   Period   Score

Objective: Read customary and metric measurements. **(Science)**

READING MEASUREMENTS

Directions: Read each customary measurement to the nearest inch
and sixteenth of an inch. Read each metric measurement to the
nearest tenth of a centimeter.

1.
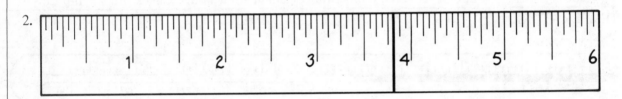

2.
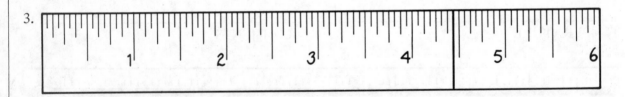

3.
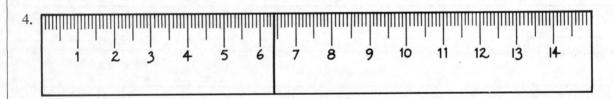

4.
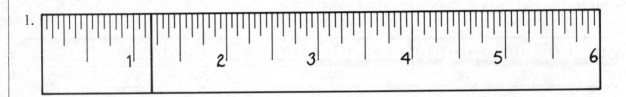

5.
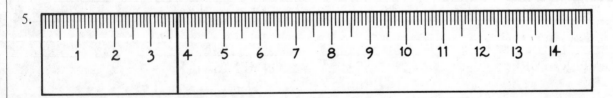

6.
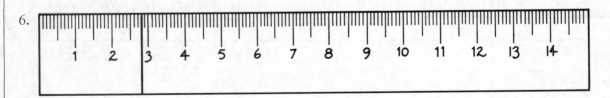

Clothing and Textiles

Name _____ Date _____ Period _____ Score _____

Objectives: Identify sources for textile fibers; use appropriate reference materials; write a paragraph of simple exposition. **(Science; Reading; Writing)**

NATURAL AND SYNTHETIC FIBERS FOR CLOTHING

Directions: In the library, find a book about textile fibers. For each kind of fiber, write whether it is natural or synthetic (manmade). If it is natural, tell where it comes from. Then choose one fiber, natural or synthetic, and write a paragraph explaining how it is made into thread and then cloth.

Fiber   Natural or Synthetic?

1. Cotton _____

2. Linen _____

3. Wool _____

4. Silk _____

5. Polyester _____

6. Rayon _____

7. Nylon _____

8. Acrylic _____

Name of fiber: _____

How it is made into thread and then cloth:

_____

_____

_____

_____

_____

_____

_____

_____

Consumer Education and Independent Living

Name   Date   Period   Score

Objectives: Study energy usage; calculate energy costs. **(Science; Math)**

ENERGY USE IN THE HOME (I)

This chart shows the average monthly use of energy, measured in kilowatt-hours (kwh) for some common household appliances. Remember that usage can vary because of larger or smaller families, the individual energy habits of families, and the climate.

Appliance	Average monthly use	Appliance	Average monthly use
Air conditioner, window unit	320 kwh	Television, color, solid state	37 kwh
Clock	2 kwh	Toaster	5 kwh
Electric clothes dryer	83 kwh	Vacuum cleaner	5 kwh
Clothes washer	10 kwh	Water heater	
Disposer	3 kwh	With a clothes washing machine in the home	450 kwh
Lights	108 kwh		
Radio	2 kwh	Without a clothes washing machine	350 kwh
Electric range	100 kwh		
Refrigerator/freezer		Electric heating	1200 kwh
Manual defrost model	95 kwh		
Frost-free model	150 kwh		

If the home has gas appliances, the family will use the following number of therms per month for their gas appliances.

Appliance	Average monthly use	Appliance	Average monthly use
Gas range	4 therms	Clothes dryer (with pilot light)	2.5 therms
Water heater		Gas heater	50 therms
With a clothes washing machine in the home	16.5 therms	Gas air conditioner	10 therms
Without a clothes washing machine	12.5 therms		

Directions: Study the energy usage charts. Then answer the following questions.

1. What uses the most energy in the home? _____

2. If a family uses their electric heater during the months of October through March, how many kilowatt hours of electricity will they use? _____

3. At the cost of $.08 per kilowatt hour, how much will they spend on heating during those months? _____

4. Another family uses their gas heater during the months of October through March. How many therms will they use? _____

5. At the cost of $.60 per therm, how much will they spend on heating during those months? _____

6. Last year, gas cost $.50 per therm. How much more will the family spend than last year, if they used the same number of therms? _____

Consumer Education and Independent Living

Name _____ Date _____ Period _____ Score _____

Objectives: Study energy usage; calculate energy costs. **(Science; Math)**

ENERGY USE IN THE HOME (II)

Directions: Study the energy usage charts from part I of this activity.
Then answer the following questions.

1. A family runs their electric air conditioner two months each year.
   At the cost of $.09 per kwh, how much will they spend for air
   conditioning during those months?
   _____

2. By setting the thermostat on their electric air conditioner
   5 degrees higher, the family can save 30 kwh per month.
   How much will they save in dollars and cents?
   _____

3. You are considering two gas ranges. The first has pilot
   lights. It costs $350.00. The second has no pilot lights.
   It operates on a spark ignition system. The pilotless
   range costs $400.00. What is the difference in cost between
   these two appliances?
   _____

4. The first range will use an average of 4 therms per month.
   How many therms will it use in a year?
   _____

5. At a cost of $.50 per therm, how much will the yearly
   gas bill be for the range?
   _____

6. A pilotless stove uses 30% less gas per year. What will the
   pilotless stove cost per year in gas bills?
   _____

7. Make a chart of expenses for each range. For the first year,
   the expenses will be the purchase price plus the cost of the
   gas. After the first year, the expense will be the cost of the gas.

	Range with pilot lights	Range without pilot lights
First year Cost of range		
Cost of gas		
Total for year		
Second year Cost of gas		
Third year Cost of gas		
Fourth year Cost of gas		
Fifth year Cost of gas		
TOTAL		

8. Extra credit: You are considering the expenses of the two ranges in problem 8. You know that gas
   prices rise every year. On a separate piece of paper, make a chart like the one in problem 8. For the
   first year, the price of gas will be $.50 per therm. However, you expect the price of gas to rise by
   $.05 per therm each year. Using your chart, calculate how much the two stoves will cost to buy
   and operate.

Careers

Objectives: Learn about calories consumed during exercise and the benefits of exercise; determine the most logical exercises to do. **(Science; Reading)**

EXERCISE ON AND OFF THE JOB

Exercise contributes to good health. Good health, in turn, makes you a better worker and a happier person. When you are out of school and working, you will be in charge of choosing the kinds of exercise you need. Often the exercise you need will depend on the kind of work you do.

Directions: Study the chart of calories consumed per hour. Then read the descriptions of the benefits of different kinds of exercise. Based on this information, answer the questions. Remember that people doing jobs that consume very few calories should do exercise that uses many calories.

Activity	Calories consumed per hour	Activity	Calories consumed per hour
Driving a car	150	Handball, racquetball	600
Playing baseball	280 (pitcher, 450)	Housework	250–350
Playing basketball	350–650	Mountain climbing	600
Bicycling	250–550	Reading	120
Rowing	250–900	Running	600–1,000
Bowling	250	Shoveling snow	400–550
Boxing	800	Skating	400–700
Brick laying	250	Skiing	500–1,000
Calisthenics	350–600	Sleeping	70
Carpentry	350–400	Swimming	350–850
Dancing	250–550	Typing	250
Golfing	250–350	Walking	120–1,000
Horseback riding	250–350	Weight training	480

Type of exercise	Benefits
Calisthenics	Builds muscles, promotes grace
Dancing	Tones muscles, joints, glands, digestive and respiratory system, refreshes the mind, gives poise.
Isometrics	Builds and tones muscles.
Jogging	Improves heart, lungs, circulatory system; tones muscles, redistributes weight.
Stretching	Increases energy and endurance, relieve aches and pains, stimulates circulation.
Walking	Improves the heart and arteries, lungs, respiratory and circulatory systems, reduces blood pressure and blood cholesterol.
Weight lifting	Strengthens muscles, prevents athletic injuries.
Competitive sport activity	Reduces stress, builds confidence; other benefits depend on the individual sport.

Careers

EXERCISE ON AND OFF THE JOB (cont.)

1. What kind(s) of exercise activity would you recommend for a person who sits and types at a word processor all day, and goes home with tired eyes and tense muscles? Explain your choice(s).

_____

_____

_____

2. What kinds of exercise would you recommend for a truck driver, who gets tired arms, legs, eyes, and general fatigue? Explain your choice(s).

_____

_____

_____

3. What kinds of exercise would benefit a laborer, who has been digging trenches and has muscle aches? Explain your choice(s).

_____

_____

_____

4. Choose an occupation. Write how the person would feel at the end of the working day, and recommend one or more kinds of exercise that would benefit that person. Explain your choice(s).

_____

_____

_____

_____

_____

_____

PART **IV**

APPENDIXES

Appendix 1

JOURNAL WRITING

Journal writing gives the students a chance to practice their writing and gives them insight into their own thoughts and feelings.

Ideally, the writing should be kept in one notebook or diary. Each day, at the beginning or closing of the class or at home, the student might write from one to four sentences, or more. It is often valuable to include famous quotations, lines from songs, etc., which have meaning to the student on a given day.

Journals can be written on many levels. At the first level, the student submits sentences which only he or she reads. At levels II and III, the student writes things which become more universal, and appropriate and valuable for others to read.

At Level IV, the entries become more formal, and at Level V, the entries are quite philosophical and may have merit as literary works. As the students read journals of famous persons and as they share their own writings with classmates, the process becomes more genuine and meaningful. It is one way to achieve insight into themselves and the world.

Journal writing is appropriate in all home economics classes. Entries reflect the students' observations, interpretations, and experiences, concerning class activities or their lives outside class. They must feel strongly about what they enter.

Prewriting experiences can involve the magic circle, class discussion, reading from a book, an observation of the situation, etc. With practice writing becomes better!

Evaluation

Evaluation may be done several times a semester. It may be quite informal; simply check to see that the students are writing. (Students should be able to fold pages over, indicating that nobody may read them.) Depending on content, a more detailed evaluation may be made. Spelling, punctuation, and sentence structure can be checked. Content may or may not be evaluated. A journal is so personal that reading it might violate privacy. This is something to be worked out with the students.

Appendix 2

WRITING FILMSTRIPS

Writing and drawing a filmstrip serves several learning purposes. First of all, the students learn to organize their thoughts. They learn to separate the important ideas from the not-so-important subtopics. Second, the students practice writing their ideas. Third, they create visual images. Fourth, they record and/or read the story. And fifth, they have audiovisual proof of the creative process!

The writing of the story is the most important part, although the students may enjoy the drawing more. The following are several prewriting activities to be done in class. Then the students write, edit, rewrite, and draw, in that order.

1. *Magic circle*

   "My favorite children's story is . . .
   "I would like to explain how to make a . . .
   "Friendships can be improved by . . .

2. *Clustering (brainstorming)*

   Have students write down a central topic, such as Cloth Toys. They then write down as many words as possible related to the making of cloth toys. Examples: cute, warm, cuddly, fat, etc. This becomes the basis for writing procedures.

Materials and Supplies Needed

1. *Clear film:* About 5' per student. This is available at a film supply shop.

2. *Pens:* Black and/or colored, the permanent type with a sharp tip. Sharpie is a good brand. They are available at art supply, stationery, or department stores.

3. *Rubbing alcohol* and *Q-tips* for correcting mistakes.

4. *Filmstrip masters:* One or more per student; see Appendix 4.

5. *Storage containers:* A cylinder, about two inches wider than the filmstrip; paper towel or wrapping paper rolls are perfect.

Appendix 3

WRITING FILMSTRIPS (STUDENT WORKSHEET)

1. Write a story about the topic you have chosen. It is important that only one idea be developed for a filmstrip. Some topics to consider:

   - a children's *story*
   - a *procedure* for making a toy
   - *ways* to improve a friendship

   Sources of ideas:

   - textbooks and library books
   - commercial filmstrips
   - children's books
   - television and radio
   - newspapers and magazines
   - life experiences

   When the story is complete and approved, you are ready to begin illustrating it.

2. Using the Filmstrip Master, draw as many frames as needed to tell your story. Each frame is 1″ wide and ¾″ high. Each picture must fit into those dimensions.

3. When the drawings are complete and approved, you are ready to transfer the pictures to clear film.

   a. Place the clear film over the drawings.

   b. Leave five or more blank frames at the beginning and ending (for threading into the projector).

   c. Trace the pictures onto the clear film, using *permanent* black and/or colored marking pens. (Sharpie is a good brand because of fine tip.) Erase mistakes with rubbing alcohol and Q-tips.

   d. Color in the shapes, as desired.

4. When the filmstrip is complete, record the story on a cassette. Pause, or use a "beep," to indicate film advance to the next frame. Read the script while showing the filmstrip.

5. Store the filmstrip in a box or tube, such as a section from a paper towel tube. Label the tube with the title, your name, and the date.

Appendix 4

FILMSTRIP MASTER (STUDENT WORKSHEET)

Title of Story _____

TOP

BEGIN

Teacher Approval _____

Appendix 5

LETTERS TO THE EDITOR

It is a thrill to see in print one's own letter to an editor!
Students could have this opportunity if they would write
a relevant, up-to-date letter.

Prewriting Experiences

1. Read and discuss newspaper articles of current interest.

2. Follow the prewriting experiences suggested in Appendix 9
   to decide upon a suitable issue for a letter to the editor of
   the local and/or school newspaper.

Writing Activities

1. Each student writes a letter to the editor on a subject
   previously discussed.

2. Have the students edit the letters and write the final
   drafts.

3. Mail the letters. If more than one letter is sent to any one
   editor, the letters should be mailed in the same envelope.

Appendix 6

CONSUMER BUSINESS LETTERS (STUDENT WORKSHEET)

A business letter is a letter written from one business to another, from a business to an individual, or from an individual to a business.

Consumer business letters are in the third category. They are letters from an individual to a business or to someone in a position of authority.

There are many kinds of consumer business letters—letters of complaint, requests for information or materials, applications for a job or college, requests for recommendations, etc.

To make the best possible impression, use the correct business letter format. The information should be clear and concise. The paragraphs should be short and to the point. The expected outcome should be stated clearly.

Type, print, or write the letter as neatly as possible. Spelling and punctuation should be perfect.

Be sure to include the following in your business letters:

1. Write your return address and the date in the upper right.
2. Next, write the name and address of the person to whom you are writing. Address your letter to a specific person whenever possible. If the company is local, telephone and ask the name of the person to whom you should write. If the company is not local, libraries have reference lists of corporations. The lists include the address of the corporation and the name of the president.
3. If you do not know the name of the person to whom you are writing, "Dear Sir/Madam:" is the correct salutation.
4. If you are typing the letter, double space between paragraphs but do not indent the first line of each paragraph. If you are using printing or writing, indent the first line of each paragraph, but do not double space.
5. Keep the paragraphs short and to the point.
6. You may send copies of the letter to other people—for example, to an appropriate consumer agency, or to the company president if you are writing to another person at that company. Write "cc: Mr. John Jones" on the left side of the letter, below the closing. And by all means, keep a copy for yourself.
7. If you need to enclose money (for any amount), DO NOT SEND CASH. Send only a personal check or money order. At the bottom of the page, write: "Enclosed: $_____ ."
8. Thank the person for considering the matter under discussion. Always be polite, but as firm as necessary.
9. Closing: Use either "Sincerely" or "Yours truly." Print or type your name in full, below the closing and your signature. If you are typing, the space between the closing and your typed name is four spaces. Sign your name in the space.

Note: If you are requesting materials or information, use the following format:

> Paragraph 1: State your purpose.
> Paragraph 2: Ask for what you want.
> Paragraph 3: Inquire if there are any other sources to aid you in obtaining additional information or material.

Appendix 7

FORMAT FOR BUSINESS LETTER

_____

_____

_____

_____

_____

_____

_____ :

_____

_____

_____

_____

_____

_____

_____

_____

_____

_____

_____

_____

_____

_____

_____

_____

_____

Appendix 8

ENVELOPE FOR BUSINESS LETTER

Appendix 9

LETTERS TO MEMBERS OF CONGRESS

The experience of writing a letter to a legislator is exciting, as well as good practice for the future. The students must write about something specific. The following activities will help in getting good writing ideas.

Prewriting Experiences

1. Show a film or filmstrip to stimulate interest in issues such as:

American Man: Tradition and Change
*Human Relationships—Why They Succeed
  or Fail*
*Re-education of Women and Men:
  Creating New Relationships*
Relationships
Human Image: Masculinity/Femininity
2000 A.D.
A Child Is a Child
The Consumer Game
Emperor's New Armor
Free to Choose
More
Your Right to a Hearing

American Woman: New Opportunities
Man and Woman: Myths and Stereotypes
Reexamining Sex Roles
Fable of He and She
We Are Woman
String Bean
Consumer Complaints the Right Way
A Day in the Life of Harvey McNeil
Foot in the Door
Harry J. Woods Is at the Door
Teenage Fathers
There Is a Law Against It
This Is Fraud

2. After the students view the film or filmstrip, discuss the issues raised.

Writing Activities

1. Have the students write a "bill of rights" for a group of people, such as children, consumers, or senior citizens.

2. Read current editorials and/or feature articles in the newspaper pertaining to one or more of these issues. (Students may bring in articles, or teachers might duplicate a recent article for all to read.)

3. Plan and write letters to appropriate legislator(s) or local government officials pertaining to the issue(s). When the final copies or letters are finished, they should be sent. Hopefully, answers will be received. If more than one letter is sent to any one person, the letters should be mailed in the same envelope.

Sample Format for Letter to Member of Congress

Date

The Honorable _____(first and last name)_____
House of Representatives/U.S. Senate
(Office address)

Dear Congressman/Congresswoman/Senator _____(last name)_____ :

Introduction — Identify yourself. (I am a student in the _____grade at
_____ School.)
— Give a brief reference to your occupation, business, or
organization.
— Thank the member of Congress for his or her support on
legislation that has benefited you, if you know of any.

Purpose of Letter — Refer to the bill by its name and number.
— Explain clearly why you support or do not support the bill.
(If supporting or opposing a particular part of the bill, refer
to that part by the bill section number.)
— Give facts and figures to support your position.

Closing — Request a reply indicating his or her position regarding your
input on the issue.
— Thank the member of Congress for his or her time and
consideration of the issue.

Sincerely,

(Signature)

(Your name, printed)
(Complete Mailing Address)

Appendix 10

ADDRESSES AND SALUTATIONS FOR PUBLIC OFFICIALS*

U.S. Officials

Washington, D.C. Office

U.S. Representative

The Honorable _____
Member of Congress

___#___ District, _____(2-letter state abbr.)_____
House Post Office
Washington, DC 20515
Dear Congressman/Congresswoman _____:

U.S. Senator

The Honorable _____

United States Senator, _____(state)_____
Senate Office Building
Washington, DC 20510
Dear Senator _____:

State Officials

Governor

The Honorable _____

Governor, State of _____(name of state)_____
State Capitol

_____(city, 2-letter state abbr., ZIP)_____

Dear Governor _____:

State Capitol Office

State Assemblyman/Assemblywoman

The Honorable _____

Assemblyman/Assemblywoman, ___#___ District

_____(name of state)_____ State Legislature
State Capitol

_____(city, 2-letter state abbr., ZIP)_____

Dear Assemblyman/Assemblywoman _____:

Local Office

The Honorable _____

Congressman/Congresswoman, ___#___ District

_____(Street address)_____

_____(city, 2-letter state abbr., ZIP)_____

Dear Congressman/Congresswoman _____:

The Honorable _____

United States Senator, _____(state)_____

_____(street address)_____

_____(city, 2-letter state abbr., ZIP)_____

Dear Senator _____:

Local Office

The Honorable _____

Assemblyman/Assemblywoman, ___#___ District

_____(street address)_____

_____(city, 2-letter state abbr., ZIP)_____

Dear Assemblyman/Assemblywoman _____:

---

*If you do not know your district number and the name of your representative,
your school office should have that information. Addresses may be found in
the telephone book.

ADDRESSES AND SALUTATIONS FOR PUBLIC OFFICIALS* (cont.)

State Senator

The Honorable _____

Senator, ___#___ District

_____(name of state)_____ State Legislature

State Capitol

_____(city, 2-letter state abbr., ZIP)_____

Dear Senator _____ :

The Honorable _____

Senator, ___#___ District

_____(street address)_____

_____(city, 2-letter state abbr., ZIP)_____

Dear Senator _____ :

Local Officials

City Councilman/Councilwoman

The Honorable _____

Councilman/Councilwoman, City of _____

_____(street address)_____

_____(city, 2-letter state abbr., ZIP)_____

Dear Councilman/Councilwoman _____ :

Mayor

The Honorable _____

Mayor, City of _____

_____(name of city)_____ City Hall

_____(street address)_____

_____(city, 2-letter state abbr., ZIP)_____

Dear Mayor _____ :

*If you do not know your district number and the name of your representative, your school office should have that information. Addresses may be found in the telephone book.

Appendix 11

WRITING DIRECTIONS, DRAWING MAPS, AND FOLLOWING MAPS

Opening Exercise

Select a well-drawn, handmade map to a location near campus. Compose written directions to go with the map. Type the directions in capital letters, using double spacing. Make a copy for each student. Cut the directions into little segments.

Have the students put the directions back together, following the map. The first student who finishes the assignment correctly wins.

Assignment

1. After the students know how to write directions to get from one location to another, they should learn how to draw a map to a particular location.

2. The student worksheet describes procedures they can follow. It would be beneficial for the students to walk to the on-campus location they have chosen. (Everyone should plan to arrive at the same location if the walk is chosen.)

3. Write the directions on the chalkboard (#3 on the student worksheet) for the off-campus location. The students are to follow your directions and draw a map of how to get there.

4. If the students actually walk to that off-campus location, some class time should be devoted to discussing any difficulties they had in following their maps.

5. After the students have written directions for going to and from their homes (#5 on student worksheet), they could plan a trip to some faraway location. Commercial maps might be needed for this exercise. As a math exercise, the students could plan the cost of driving, or going by bus, to their chosen destination.

This exercise can have long-term personal and social benefits.

Optional

It would be fun for the students to exchange directions and maps and then try to get to various locations by following each other's maps.

Appendix 12

WRITING DIRECTIONS, DRAWING MAPS, AND FOLLOWING MAPS (STUDENT WORKSHEET)

Following correct procedures:

1. Write the directions for going to a destination on campus, starting in your present classroom. The following information should help you write good directions. Be sure:

   - directions (north, left, etc.) are included

   - sequences are correct.

   - all street names are given.

   - blocks (miles) to be traveled are given.

   - the street address and telephone number are included at the bottom.

   - the map is oriented correctly: that is, north must always be at the top of the map.

   - important landmarks, signal lights, etc. are included.

2. Draw a map for going to the destination, starting in your present classroom.

3. Draw a map to a nearby off-campus location, following the directions as written on the blackboard.

4. If possible, walk to the location, following the map you have drawn. Write down your reactions to following your map.

5. Write the directions and draw a map of how to go from your home to school.

6. Draw a map (use a city map if you travel by bus any great distance) for returning home from school.

Appendix 13

WRITING LISTS: STEPS IN A PROCESS

In every home economics class, the process of doing something is as important as the end result. When the students can write the steps for completing a process, they not only will know the procedure itself, but will have the ability to show others how to complete it. These are valuable, lifetime skills.

Learning Activities

1. The teacher (or a student) demonstrates a simple process. (See the list of suggestions in the Teacher-Managed Writing Activities for each subject area.)

2. The students list everything the demonstrator does or uses, including supplies and equipment.

3. Discuss the lists, making sure all relevant information has been included.

4. The students rewrite the information in easy-to-understand, numbered steps.

5. Finally, the students write a two or three paragraph composition describing the procedures for the process. This is actually the most valuable part of the writing process.

Optional

6. When they finish writing the lists, the students can exchange their direction sheets and actually perform the process (a great and funny exercise, especially for something such as making peanut butter sandwiches).

Appendix 14

ADVERTISING

Writing an ad is a good exercise for the students, especially if it incorporates their own experiences. If the students learn how to make attractive posters to promote something in a school organization, they will have learned something of practical value. Studying advertisements can prepare the students to psychologically resist advertising pressures. (Writing an ad to sell a product commercially is too difficult for students. Highly experienced media people work as teams to create radio, television, and printed ad campaigns. This task is far beyond the reach of secondary students.)

Prewriting Experiences

Have students study ads on television or in magazines and newspapers. Discuss why some ads are more appealing than others and what products students have purchased because of advertising. (Toothpaste is a good example. Each student mentions the brand he or she uses. Write the brand on the board. When a duplicate is named, add an extra slash mark. The students will quickly understand the role of advertising on themselves.)

The student worksheet provides information that can be used as the basis for creating outstanding posters.

Supplies Needed

Plain paper, construction paper, poster (tag) board; pencils, rulers, marking pens; magazines for cutting pictures; plus extras such as yarn, shiny paper, etc.

PART V

ANSWER KEY FOR PARTS II AND III ACTIVITIES

Answer Key

Foods and Nutrition

A Cooking Dictionary
(p. 38)

1. a
2. a
3. b
4. a

Reading and Understanding
Directions (p. 39)

1. a
2. d
3. b
4. d
5. a
6. d

Learning to Measure
(p. 40)

1. pack
2. dry
3. glass/pyrex/clear/plastic
4. sifted
5. divide
6. 3
7. 16
8. displacement

Analyzing Labels for
Information (p. 41)

1. 4 grams
2. 140 calories
3. flour
4. a. Vitamin A
   b. Vitamin C
5. 1402
6. Dubuque, Iowa
7. BHA, BHT
8. 2½ servings
9. Thiamine mononitrate

Comparison of Food Prices
(p. 42)

Answers will vary.

Snack Food Analysis
(p. 43)

Answers will vary.

Comparing Canned Foods
(p. 46)

Answers will vary.

Making Metric Punch
(p. 47)

Total: 1,000 ml
1. 250 ml
2. frozen lemonade and
   fruit punch
3. water and orange juice
4. a. 50 ml
   b. 100 ml

Metric Weight at the
Grocery Store (p. 48)

1. b
2. b
3. a
4. c

Using Metric and Customary
Units (p. 49)

1. Customary: 180 sq. ft.,
   42 sq. in.
   Metric: 180,000 sq. cm
2. Customary: 12 lb. 3 oz.
   Metric: 4.87 kg 650 g
3. Customary: 2 gal. 2 qt.
   ½ pt.
   Metric: 10 l 250 ml

Recipe Math (p. 50)

Cheesecake ingredients

	Doubled	Halved
1.	10	2½
2.	6	1½
3.	8	2
4.	1	¼
5.	½	⅛
6.	3½	¾ c + 2 T
7.	3	¾

Spinach Loaf ingredients

	Doubled	Halved
1.	1½	⅜
2.	2	½
3.	2	½
4.	4	1
5.	4	1
6.	2	½
7.	1	¼

Reconstituting Milk (p. 51)

1. a
2. c
3. a
4. b

Mrs. Rosen's Sugar Cookies
(p. 52)

1. b
2. c
3. b
4. c

Planning a Family Food Budget
(p. 53)

1. $75
2. 33%; 16%; 20%; 15%; 16%
3. $7

Orange Juice Comparison (p. 54)

1. a	4. a
2. b	5. b
3. b	6. b

Figuring Unit Pricing (p. 55)

1. a. $ .05 *
   b. .07
2. a. .03 *
   b. .04
3. a. .13
   b. .12 *
4. a. .14
   b. .09 *
5. a. .06
   b. .05 *

Comparison Shopping (p. 56)

1. a
2. a
3. b
4. b
5. a
6. a
7. $4.41
8. $4.59
9. $3.50

Eating at a Restaurant or Eating at Home: A Cost Comparison (p. 56)

$ 5.70 subtotal for one person
 11.40 subtotal for two people
   .68 6% sales tax
  1.71 15% tip
$13.79 total cost for two people

1. $ 4.00
2.   9.79
3.   717.08
4.   208.00
5.   509.08

	Cost per Serving	Price for Two
Lettuce	$ .06	$ .12
Dressing	.10	.20
Turkey	.22	.44
Ham	.25	.50
Cheese	.23	.46
Tomato	.15	.30
Eggs	.07	.14
Rolls	.16	.32
Jelly	.03	.06
Soup	.15	.30
Crackers	.03	.06
Cake	.43	.86
Coffee	.05	.10
Butter	.07	.14
TOTAL	$2.00	$4.00

Parenting and Family Relationships

Invitation (p. 67)

1. c
2. b
3. b, d
4. a
5. b, c

Understanding Temperature Readings (p. 68)

1. a
2. a
3. b
4. a

Happy Birthday (p. 81)

The Zoo: $14.00
Happy Mountain Park: $59.75
Fantasy Park: $50.00
Stars' Studio Tour: $47.25

Rock Concert Tickets (p. 82)

1. $28.00
2. $19.00
3. $41.00
4. $20.00
5. $18.00
6. $6.00
7. $19.00
8. Answers will vary.

How Much Will the Wedding Cost? (p. 83)

1. Country club $4,855
   Church and reception $2,130
   Church and sweet table $1,780
   Home and reception $1,085
2. Home and reception
3. Any except country club
4. c
5. $4.00
6. Answers will vary.

Planning a Budget (p. 85)

Rent and utilities	$ 570
Food	285
Transportation	228
Medical and dental	152
Clothing	285
Savings	190
Other	190
Grand Total	$1900

Renting an Apartment (p. 86)

1. $1090
2. $1520
3. $1770
4. The apartment would cost $715 with utilities, which is 38% of their take-home pay. They would need to skimp on other things to cover this increased cost. In addition, it would cost $290 extra at the time they signed their lease.

Researching the Cost of Baby Foods (p. 87)

Answers will vary.

Landmarks in Baby's Growth (p. 88)

Answers will vary.

Selecting Infant Clothing (p. 90)

1. c
2. a
3. b
4. c
5. a
6. b

Ages at Which Shots Should Be Given (p. 91)

D/P/T:
   July 5, 1985
   Sept. 5, 1985
   Nov. 5, 1985
   Nov. 5, 1986
   May 5, 1989–May 5, 1991
Polio:
   July 5, 1985
   Sept. 5, 1985
   Nov. 5, 1986
   May 5, 1989–May 5, 1991
Measles: Aug. 5, 1986
Rubella: Aug. 5, 1986
Mumps: Aug. 5, 1986
D/T:
   May 6, 1999–May 5, 2000

Clothing and Textiles

Pattern Symbols (p. 97)

1. b   3. c
2. a   4. a

Understanding Classifications
(p. 98)

1. spool
2. pleats
3. seam roll
4. needle
5. tailor tack
6. back stitch
7. polyester
8. hemmer
9. linen
10. fusible web

Understanding This Pattern Envelope (p. 99)

1. 4⅛ yd
2. 3⅜ yd
3. obvious diagonals
4. no
5. side seam
6. with nap, shading, pile, or one-way design
7. (any one listed)
8. Superior Patterns
   175 West 79th Street
   New York, NY 10024

Parts of the Bernina Sewing Machine (p. 101)

1. Feed dog
2. Needle throat plate
3. Sewing foot
4. Needle clamp
5. Thread guide
6. Light cover
7. Light switch
8. Thread take-up lever
9. Bobbin winder tension
10. Thread tension discs and slot
11. Tension indicator window
12. Tension centering wheel
13. Spool pins
14. Bobbin winder spindle
15. Handwheel (flywheel)
16. Handwheel release
17. Needle position control knob
18. Stitch width knob
19. Stitch length regulator/ reverse lever
20. Satin stitch stop lever
21. Satin stitch and buttonhole regulator
22. Control knob for drop feed
23. Free arm
24. Presser foot lever
25. Bobbin case cover

Parts of the Elna Sewing Machine
(p. 102)

1. Free arm
2. Sewing foot
3. Rotary hook cover
4. Light
5. Presser foot lever
6. Upper thread tension dial
7. Thread take-up lever
8. Thread guides
9. Needle-position wheel
10. Stitch width knob
11. Automatic stitch selector dial
12. Reverse lever
13. Stitch length regulator
14. Spool pins
15. Bobbin winder spindle
16. Flywheel
17. Flywheel release
18. Light switch
19. Foot control

Parts of the Singer Sewing Machine
(p. 103)

1. Spool pin
2. Spool pin felt
3. Bobbin winder tension discs
4. Take-up lever
5. Pressure regulating dial
6. Threading chart
7. Thread cutter
8. Presser foot
9. Needle (throat) plate
10. Presser foot lever
11. Bobbin
12. Bobbin case tension screw
13. Slide plate
14. Thread tension dial
15. Light
16. Throat plate position lever
17. Stitch length regulator
18a. Stop-motion nut
18b. Handwheel (flywheel)
19. Power and light switch
20. Bobbin winder thread post
21. Bobbin winder latch and spindle
22. Electrical connections and speed controller

What's the Best Buy?
(p. 112)

1. a
2. c
3. a
4. b

Recognizing Measurements (p. 113)

A. 1. – 2''   6. – 1⅛''
   2. – 1''   7. – 1¼''
   3. – ⅝''   8. – 1⅝''
   4. – ¼''   9. – 2⅛''
   5. – ¾''   10. – 2½''

B. 1. – ⅝''
   2. – 2½''
   3. – ¼''
   4. – ½''
   5. – 1''
   6. – ⅜''
   7. – 1½''
   8. – 2¾''
   9. – 3³⁄₁₆''
  10. – ⅞''

Fractions in the Clothing Class
(p. 114)

1. ½''   4. ⁴⁄₈''
2. ⅝''   5. ⅞''
3. ½''   6. 2¾''

How Much Will It Cost? (p. 115)

1. c
2. d
3. d
4. b
5. a

Buying Notions (p. 116)

1. c
2. c
3. b
4. a

Needlepoint Pillows: How Much
Do They Cost? (p. 117)

1. 4   6. 9
2. $1.10   7. $14.63 ($14.70
3. $33.00 ($32.93   is acceptable)
   is acceptable) 8. $4.87
4. $5.91   9. $5.36
5. $7.01

How Much Can You Save
by Sewing? (p. 118)

Total value of your time:
   $11.85 (in 2 places)
Cost to sew pants:
   $41.00
Difference:
   $11.95

How Long Does It Take?
(p. 119)

1. b
2. b
3. c
4. d

The Cost of Making Vests (I), (II)
(pp. 120–121)

1. 10
2. 27
3. 14
4. 51
5. 7.5
6. 18
7. 10
8. 35.5
9. $39.80
10. $34.90
11. $4.90
12. $177.99
13. $170.05
14. $7.94
15. $2.37
16. $2.77
17. $3.16
18. $23.70
19. $49.86 (or $49.77
    is acceptable)
20. $25.28

The Cost of Making Vests (I), (II)
(cont.)

21. $98.84 (or $98.75)
22. $268.89 (or $268.78)
23. $16.13
24. $285.02 (or $284.91)
25. $7.92 (or $7.91)

Alterations: Will They Pay?
(p. 122)

Answers will vary.

**Consumer Education and
Independent Living**

Guarantee (p. 133)

1. b
2. d
3. a
4. d
5. c

Can You Identify These Consumer
Protection Laws? (p. 135)

1. C
2. D
3. I
4. G
5. A
6. B
7. E
8. F
9. H
10. J
11. G
12. H
13. K

Shopping by Mail (p. 137)

1. $23.00
2. $13.79
3. $9.21
4. snap closure
5. camel
6. polyester fiber fill

Name of item (1 or 2 words)	Complete Catalog number	How many (Pkgs, etc.)	Color Number	Size	Price for one	Total	Ship wt. lbs.	oz.
Reversible vest	HB 516-2516 B	2		M	13.79	27.58	3	4

	Total	tot. lbs.	tot. oz.
Total for goods	27.58		
Tax	1.65		
Transportation and handling	1.50	3	4
Owed on previous cash orders		total wt. in lbs.	
Cash price	30.73		4
Amount Enclosed — Check, money order — Refund drafts	30.73		

What Does This Gas Bill
Tell You? (p. 145)

1. 01-4557-935-6393-8
2. Feb. 1, 1980–Mar. 4, 1980
3. 5858
4. 5970
5. 119
6. $3.10
7. $.06694
8. $1.68
9. 5%
10. 1.8

Understanding a Water and
Power Bill (I) (p. 146)

1. $93.80
2. 64
3. 1,237
4. 25
5. 5%
6. $1.50

Understanding a Water and
Power Bill (II) (p. 147)

1. 1/12/78   3. 1,361
2. 2,829   4. 23,188

Using Utility Bill Customer
Information (p. 148)

1. right to left
2. counterclockwise
3. 100; 10
4. 1,000; 10,000; 100,000 cu. ft.
5. 7.48
6. 7240.64 gal.

Comparative Pricing (p. 153)

1. c   4. b
2. a   5. b
3. b

Spending Your Birthday Money (p. 154)

1. Suit B
2. A. $8.68; $132.63
   B. 8.15; 124.64
   C. 8.40; 128.35
3. Suit A
4. A—11%; B—7%, C—8%
5. Answers will vary.

Spending Money by Percentages and Fractions (p. 155)

1. Food $ 2.80
   Clothing   2.00
   Savings   .80
   Other   2.40
   Total $ 8.00

2. Food/School $22.50
   Clothes   11.25
   Savings   2.25
   Other   9.00
   Total $45.00

3. Food $ 3.30
   Records   1.65
   Savings/Jacket   3.30
   Cosmetics   4.13
   Savings/Trip   4.12
   Total $16.50

4. Bus $ 4.00
   Entertainment   5.00
   Food   2.00
   Savings   9.00
   Total $20.00

Interested in Interest? (p. 156)

1. $ .03
2. $ .50
3. $ .25
4. $1.00
5. $7.20
6. $3.60, $4.50, $ .45

Computing Simple Interest (p. 157)

1. $ .90
2. $ 42.00
3. $487.50
4. $ 6.00
5. $335.00
6. $ 90.00

The Cost of Credit (p. 158)

A. $ 4.58
B. $69.00; $4.00
C. $97.80; $22.80

1. Plan B
2. $ .58
3. $18.80
4. Answers will vary.
5. Plan B (cheapest)
6. Answers will vary.

Bank Account (p. 160)

1. $400
2. $52.00
3. $11.25
4. $310.30
5. $1,000
6. 30 weeks

Credit Cards (p. 161)

Sales Slip

1	belt	9.98	9.98
1	slacks	18.98	18.98
1	shirt	15.00	15.00
		sub total	43.96
		tax	2.64
		total	46.60

1. a
2. c

Room Floor Plan (p. 162)

1. c
2. d
3. b
4. c

Reading a Graph (p. 163)

1. b
2. c
3. b
4. a

Planning a Holiday (p. 164)

1. $420
2. $105
3. $125
4. $650
5. $325
6. $225 more expensive to drive
7. Answers will vary.

Buying Sports Equipment (p. 165)

1. $116.00
2. $ 2.94
3. $188.68
4. $ 4.86
5. $ 22.26
   $ 27.74
6. $ 25.80

The High Cost of Shoplifting (p. 166)

1. $84.50
2. 20
3. 10
4. $3.00
5. $18.00
6. 72
7. $2.40
8. $3,000
9. the customer
10. bankruptcy

Careers

Classified Ads: Help Wanted (p. 176)

1. a. banquet experience
   b. Food and Beverage Director
   c. no
2. a. Maine
   b. no, June–October
3. a. Miami
   b. nouvelle cuisine
   c. low-calorie French cooking
   d. no
   e. chef

Figuring Mileage (p. 186)

1. b
2. a
3. b
4. c

Calculating Sales Tax (p. 187)

Sweater	$1.28	$ 17.23
Blouse	1.60	21.55
Polo shirt	.96	12.91
Shoes	2.24	30.24
Vest	1.44	19.39
Coat	8.00	107.99
Jacket	4.00	53.95
Suit	8.80	118.75
Jeans	2.64	35.59
Scarf	.47	6.36
Pants	1.80	24.30

Time and Wage Concepts (p. 188)

1.
Gross	$214.00
F.I.C.A.	14.34
Federal	42.80
State	6.42
Credit Union	15.00
Net	135.44

2.
Monday	8 hours
Tuesday	8 hours
Wednesday	6 hours
Thursday	8 hours
Saturday	9½ hours
Total	39½ hours

Gross	$132.33
F.I.C.A.	8.98
Federal	26.80
State	4.02
Credit Union	.00
Net	$ 92.53

Calculating Wage Deductions (p. 189)

Regular hours	$152.00
Overtime	17.10
Gross pay	169.10

Deductions:

a.	$ 5.07
b.	33.82
c.	11.33
d.	1.35
e.	10.00
Tot.	$61.57

Net Pay: $107.53

Computing Your Wage (p. 190)

1. $54.40; $70.00
2. a. $272.00; $350.00
   b. $272.00; $350.00
3. $14,144.00; $18,200.00
4. $4,056

	Weekly	Yearly
Cosmetologist:	$214	$11,128
Child Care Aide:	$180	$ 9,360
Cashier:	$150	$ 7,800
Pattern Cutter:	$330	$17,160

Extra Credit

1. $147 per week
2. $7,644 per year

Cost of Deli Favorites (I) (p. 191)

1. Total cost of foods in column C: $37.24

2-3.
Item	Unit cost	One serving
Bread	$ .02	$ .04
Ham	.12	.24
Cheese	.08	.16
Mayonnaise	.01	.01
Mustard	.04	.02
Pickles	.11	.11
Lettuce	.27	.03
Tomatoes	.16	.08
Radishes	.17	.02
Cucumbers	.25	.03
Dressing	.03	.09
Milk	.10	.05
Ice Cream	.13	.07
Sauce	.07	.07

4. Total cost of one serving: $1.02

Cost of Deli Favorites (II) (p. 192)

1. $127.50
2. a. $575.00
   b. 34.50
   c. 609.50
3. a. 447.50
   b. 335.63
4. $111.87
5. Answers will vary.

Student-Managed Activities in Science

Food Additives (I) (p. 195)

1. Aluminum calcium silicate: anticaking agent for salt (S).
2. Ammonium chloride: yeast food or dough conditioner for bread (S)
3. Annatto: coloring and flavoring for peaches, baked goods, and dairy products (O).
4. Aspartame: non-caloric sweetener (F).
5. Calcium disodium (EDTA): preservative for flavor, color, texture (F).
6. Calcium propionate: mold inhibitor for baked goods. (F).
7. Carotene: coloring for dairy products (S).
8. Guar gum: stabilizer and binder (O).
9. Lactic acid: flavoring—adds acidic flavor; also used in infant formulas (S).
10. Mannitol: texturizer and sweetener (F).

Food Additives (II) (p. 196)

1. Monosodium glutamate: flavoring for meats, condiments, etc. (F)
2. Nitrates: color fixative in processed meats (F).
3. Nitrites: color fixative and preservative in processed meats (F).
4. Polysorbate 80: (sorbitan monostearate): emulsifier, defoaming, and flavor-dispersing in sweets, whipped toppings, and artificial creamers (S).
5. Propylene glycol: color preservative for sweets and meat (S).
6. Potassium chloride: substitute for salt (F).
7. Saccharin: artificial sweetener (F).
8. Sodium benzoate: preservative used in margarine, fish, and sweets (S).
9. Sodium bisulfite: bleaching agent for wine, beer, shellfish, fresh fruits and vegetables (F—causes toxic effects in some people).
10. Sorbitol: sugar substitute (F).

The Importance of Vitamins (p. 197)

1. A: Helps eyes and skin, helps fight infections. Leafy green vegetables, carrots.
2. B_1: Maintains nervous system, stabilizes appetite, stimulates growth. Wheat germ, blackstrap molasses, bran.
3. B_2: Helps formation of antibodies and red blood cells. Liver, tongue, brewer's yeast.
4. B_6: Helps formation of antibodies and balance of blood fluids. Meat, whole grains, brewer's yeast.
5. B_{12}: Helps blood cells and nervous system. Meat, fish, dairy products.

The Importance of Vitamins (p. 197) (cont.)

6. B_{13}: Helps metabolism of other B vitamins.
Root vegetables.
7. Biotin: Helps in metabolism and in using other B vitamins.
Egg yolk, beef liver, unpolished rice.
8. C: Helps healing, blood vessels, resistance to infections, absorption of iron.
Fresh fruits and vegetables.
9. D: Helps nervous system, helps absorption of calcium and phosphorus.
Sunlight.
10. E: Helps blood cells, prevents unwanted clotting, aids cell respiration.
Cold-pressed vegetable oil, raw nuts and seeds, soybeans.
11. Niacin: Helps skin, tongue, digestive system, metabolism.
Meat, poultry, fish, peanuts.
12. Folic Acid: Helps red blood cells, cell growth, and protein metabolism.
Leafy green vegetables, liver.
13. Pantothenic Acid: Helps formation of fat, energy release, and utilization of other vitamins.
Organ meats, egg yolks, whole grains.

The Importance of Minerals (p. 198)

1. Calcium: Helps bones, teeth, blood clotting, muscles, nerves, and heart.
Dairy products, bone meal.
2. Phosphorus: Helps bones, teeth, and utilization of other minerals.
3. Iodine: Helps prevent goiter, regulate metabolism; is part of hormone thyroxine.
Fish, kelp.
4. Iron: Helps form hemoglobin and myoblobin, helps protein metabolism.
Organ meats, leafy green vegetables.

5. Magnesium: Helps utilize other nutrients.
Fresh green vegetables, apples, almonds.
6. Manganese: Helps the skeletal system and development of sexual hormones.
Egg yolks, whole grains, fresh green vegetables.
7. Zinc: Helps produce insulin, helps digest phosphorus, and aids healing.
Proteins, whole grains, pumpkin seeds.
8. Potassium: Helps heart muscles, nervous system, and kidneys.
Vegetables, bananas, oranges, whole grains, potatoes.

Reading a Thermometer (p. 199)

2. 100.6—Low fever—take temperature again in a few hours. Check other symptoms.
3. 103.8—high fever—call the doctor.
4. 97.3—below normal—usual for person who is almost well again.
5. 98.6—normal.

Reading Measurements (p. 200)

1. $1\frac{3}{16}''$
2. $3\frac{13}{16}''$
3. $4\frac{7}{16}''$
4. 6.4 cm
5. 3.7 cm
6. 2.8 cm

Natural and Synthetic Fibers for Clothing (p. 201)

1. Cotton: Natural—plant fiber
2. Linen: Natural—plant fiber
3. Wool: Natural—animal coat fiber
4. Silk: Natural—cocoon of silkworm
5. Polyester: Synthetic
6. Rayon: Synthetic
7. Nylon: Synthetic
8. Acrylic: Synthetic

Energy Use in the Home (I) (p. 202)

1. heater
2. 7200 kwh
3. $576.00
4. 300 therms
5. $180
6. $30

Energy Use in the Home (II) (p. 203)

1. $57.60
2. $ 5.40
3. $50.00
4. 48 therms
5. $24.00
6. $16.80

7.

	pilots	pilotless
1st yr		
range	350.00	400.00
gas	24.00	16.80
total	374.00	416.80
2nd yr		
gas	24.00	16.80
3rd yr		
gas	24.00	16.80
4th yr		
gas	24.00	16.80
5th yr		
gas	24.00	16.80
total	$470.00	$484.00

8.

	pilots	pilotless
1st yr		
range	350.00	400.00
gas	24.00	16.80
total	374.00	416.80
2nd yr		
gas	26.40	18.48
3rd yr		
gas	28.80	20.16
4th yr		
gas	31.20	21.84
5th yr		
gas	33.60	23.52
total	$494.00	$500.80